BERMUDA'S BOTANICAL WONDERLAND

A Field Guide

Christine Watlington

Foreword by

Dr David Wingate

5-13-09

INSCRIBED FOR BARBARA
HAPPY PLANT HUNTING —
SO GOOD TO MEET YOU
ALL BEST
WISHES
Christine
(THE AUTHOR)

First published 1996 by
MACMILLAN EDUCATION LTD
London and Oxford
Companies and representatives throughout the world

www.macmillan-caribbean.com

ISBN-13: 978-0-333-60652-0
ISBN-10: 0-333-60652-3

2011 2010 2009 2008 2007 2006
14 13 12 11 10 9 8 7 6 5 4 3

This book is printed on paper suitable for recycling and made from fully managed and sustained forest sources.

Printed in Thailand

A catalogue record for this book is available from the British Library

Cover illustrations by Christine Watlington

basic floral structures

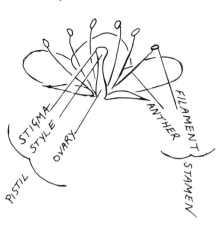

STIGMA
STYLE
OVARY
PISTIL
ANTHER
FILAMENT
STAMEN

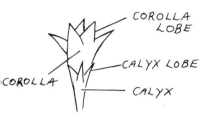

COROLLA
LOBE
CALYX LOBE
CALYX
COROLLA

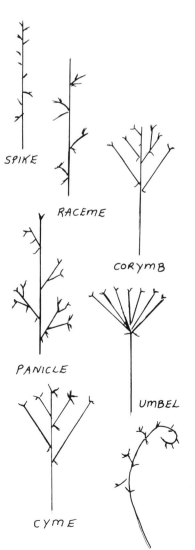

SPIKE

RACEME

CORYMB

PANICLE

UMBEL

CYME

SCORPIOID CYME

Contents

simple leaf shapes

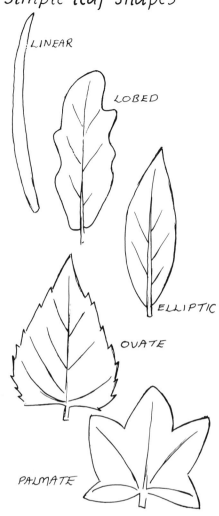

LINEAR
LOBED
ELLIPTIC
OVATE
PALMATE

compound leaf shapes

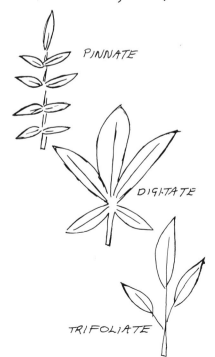

PINNATE
DIGITATE
TRIFOLIATE

Acknowledgements

Thank you to my loved ones who are totally supportive, to my dearest daughter Victoria who at five is learning plant names and studies nature with great joy and interest, and thank you to our beloved Thomas Watlington. Also to my dearest Mother who is so kind and wise and my dear sisters, and to the treasured memories of our Father Philip William Pill. My love of nature stems directly from glorious childhood memories filled with wildflowers in the unspoilt ancient countryside of Devon, England.

Thank you to Barry Phillips for his generous time helping me with plant identification in this book. More than this, he has enriched my plant knowledge for many years, from early days while studying at the Royal Botanical Gardens, Kew and later while he spent 10 years in Bermuda. As Bermuda's Government horticulturalist he achieved so much for the Islands' plantworld. His plant knowledge is superlative; Barry set out to help save the Bermuda Cedar Tree. With his propagation knowledge he soon was able to introduce thousands of new Cedar plants into the Islands' landscape. He is still known locally as 'Mr Plant one on me'.

Thank you also to John Whitehead, an incredible plantsman and friend, for checking my final index and updating some of the plant names in it.

I am also very grateful to Dr David Wingate for his 'foreword' and his inspiration. I have been so aware of David's perseverance and personal quest for lovingly caring for Bermuda's bird and plant life. It is not only David's job it is his life commitment. He has nurtured so many of Bermuda's wild areas it is hard to imagine what would have happened without this remarkable man's devotion, not forgetting to thank him for his invaluable list of plants in their habitats (when I thought my work was finished!) and then for his stories of new plants appearing close to the runway at the airport – proof that nothing is ever at an end but everything is evolving....

My sincere thanks to staff at the Royal Botanical Gardens, Kew for resolving some of the final botanical mysteries. Kew is home for the world of plants, I feel very fortunate to have spent three years there.

Then not least to my dear Richard Hartley who has recently come along on trips exploring local habitats and, like all plant lovers, does not find the obsession for plants odd.

Finally a special thank you to Bill Lennox, Director of Macmillan Caribbean, for making this book possible, and the staff involved who have all been so helpful.

Christine Watlington (née Pill)

When studying plants in the field, the following points should be noted:

Size and type of plant: tree, shrub, herbaceous, annual, biennial, perennial, climbing or low spreading, evergreen or deciduous.

Arrangement and type of leaves: whether opposite or alternate, stalked or toothed, serrated or smooth, hairy or hairless.

Type of stem, twig or bark: woody or succulent, smooth or furrowed, flat buds or protruding, climbing or procumbent (lying on the ground).

Flower: shape and colour, number of petals and sepals (are they jointed?), stamen and style (one or many?).

Preface

Painting plants and wildlife brings one so close to the wonders of nature. I hope that my sketches and studies will help others gain a deeper understanding of Bermuda's plants and their habitats. Hopefully this will then help in protecting the Bermuda flora that is suffering a great demise.

While growing up in the English countryside, I could never have imagined the feeling of panic I now feel when I see or read about land being destroyed. Wildlife seemed as safe as it was wondrous. My first memory of the lovely Bermuda Islands was that of a tiny gem amidst an endless ocean. Once on terra firma the web of lush vegetation looked gigantic and quite formidable. Then I noted that some of the enormous plants were giant versions of plants I had seen under glass in the great botanical gardens of Europe.

The plant world for me has always evoked a great joy, fascination and humility. In the 1970s I worked at the Royal Botanical Gardens, Kew and the Royal Horticultural Society Garden, Wisley. Being a part of, and discovering the world of plants made me a devoted conservationist. The range of live and dried plant specimens there, including historical and modern-day information, is massive. The dedicated scientists who discover new food and medicinal plants, along with hardy botanists who risk life and limb travelling to far flung places in search of new species, instilled in me a great desire to study the wonders of nature.

So many dedicated people all over the world are now working to protect the earth's plants and wildlife. Bermuda is enriched with a good share of these people. My introduction to Bermuda began in 1977 when Dr David Wingate and Barry Phillips took me on what seems today rather like a kaleidoscope of exploration of Bermuda's wild areas.

These magical first glances, along with the obvious acts of love and dedication that had been put into protecting Bermuda's natural world, touched me so much, I felt immediately that I wanted to help in some way with the ongoing task of preserving Bermuda's open space and wildlife. (I wish sometimes that I had more time to start the work over again.)

This book is not intended as a comprehensive botanical treatise. Rather, it has been my intention to capture the essence of Bermuda as revealed in its flora.

The love I have for the small areas of wilderness still surviving is so total that the images of Bermuda's beauty will stay with me forever.

Christine Watlington (née Pill)

Foreword

When Christine Watlington first asked me to review the draft of her book on Bermuda flora, in the hope that I would write a foreword, I had no idea what an incredible wealth of botanical illustrations this talented artist had compiled over the seventeen years since she moved to Bermuda.

There had been no *comprehensive* illustrated guide to Bermuda botany since the work of Nathaniel, Lord Britton, published in 1918. All available published guides since that time have provided only superficial treatment by illustrating a few of the most spectacular exotics in colour. Here, at last is a work which includes virtually all of Bermuda's flora *and* is illustrated in colour by a professional botanical illustrator.

This work could easily stand alone as an artistic creation, evoking the essence of Bermuda in its vignettes of traditional Bermuda landscapes which accompany each chapter heading and in its simple text, written straight from the heart, which clearly reveals the powerful impact that Bermuda's intense natural beauty has had on the author. Indeed, Christine's artwork and style bring to mind that classic work by Edith Holden *The Country Diary of an Edwardian Lady*.

But as a *guidebook* it achieves much more than this. By her own admission Christine is not a professional botanist, but she has made every effort to consult with professionals to be sure that her illustrations are correctly identified with the most up-to-date botanical names.

Perhaps, above all, this book will serve as a time capsule of a golden era in Bermuda's history when the growing profusion of exotic introduction still left some room for the island's unique endemic heritage – an era now gravely threatened by rampant development, lawnmowers, weed whacker herbicides, and loss of biodiversity.

Visitors and Bermudians alike will find endless pleasure in taking this book into the field on their rambles of discovery. To the extent that it enhances their appreciation for nature's boundless beauty and diversity, it may very well serve as a catalyst to turn the tide in favour of conservation. Bermuda is indeed fortunate to have benefited from Christine's long labour of love.

David B. Wingate
Conservation Officer,
Department of Agriculture,
Fisheries and Parks.

1. Introduction

Why plants are so important

Generally we do not contemplate why and how we happen to survive in the system of life on earth, but if we could see our world from a cosmic view, we would be more aware of the wonders, riches and miracles that carpet the earth. To have that view of nature (a bird's-eye-view) would be remarkable. Today, nature is sometimes ignored by busy people surviving everyday life in a hectic world.

The green blankets of foliage on earth give us life – 90 per cent of our food comes from plants. Plants are an essential component of man's survival for life on earth, providing us with the very air we breath. They help to protect us against pollution, including noise, and give us a shady place to sit on a hot sunny day.

From the early days of Cook and Darwin, mankind has had an insatiable desire to further understand the plant world. Although today we have a wealth of medicines from plants, research is constantly finding new species for food and medicine, and new discoveries are still being made by collectors and scientists, which may provide cures for major medical problems in the future.

Today, the World Wide Fund for Nature, along with many other enlightened and dedicated conservation groups and individuals, strives to bring the world a growing knowledge of how to protect our environment. By supporting conservation groups on a local and international basis, we all play a part in reducing the loss of forests and plants around the world.

The Islands

Some of the remotest islands in the world and the most northerly coral reef in the world, Bermuda today is a busy, cosmopolitan community, very accessible with regular planes and ships.

The pastel-coloured homes with bright white rooftops, which form Bermuda's unique architecture, create an impression quite different from anywhere else in the world. Bermudians paint their rooftops every year, keeping them clean as they catch rainwater for each household.

Well over half a million tourists visit Bermuda every year, and the city of Hamilton has many wonderful shops and numerous points of interest. There are lovely gardens everywhere, National Trust properties, many art galleries, including the National Gallery in the City Hall, the Cathedral and many other churches, the Bermuda library, the Parliament buildings and the Botanical Gardens. From ferries travelling the Great Sound, the wooded landscape can be seen. At the western end the Royal Naval Dockyard has been carefully developed, and includes the Maritime Museum, shopping mall, craft market, restaurants and pubs. At the eastern end of the Island there is the world-renowned Biological Station for research. Currently studying ocean temperatures and global warming, people and scientists come from all over the world to attend courses. The Aquarium Museum and Zoo depict Bermuda's natural history in a wonderful setting. The Old Town of St George's, with its tiny lanes and historical buildings and museums, should not be forgotten. It was here that the Island was first settled after the wrecking of the *Sea Venture* in 1609. So much culture, including Gombay dancers, thrives amidst lush tropical vegetation and unique wildlife habitats.

The Islands are full of activity. There are yacht races, horseback riding, carriage rides, water sports and boat tours. The old railway line, which ran from one end of the Island to the other, is today a lovely nature trail for walking and for cyclists.

Bermuda is fortunate to have many dedicated groups helping to protect the environment: the National Trust, Audubon Society, Garden Club, Botanical Society, Horticultural Society, Bermuda Aquarium, Biological Station, K.B.B. and others.

A tiny lane in St George's – still, quiet and tranquil. The wildfowl feel quite safe to venture along the roadside, collecting insects en route.

An old wooden shack in Somerset – quite a rare sight today! Locals now live in modern houses with pretty white roofs and greet visitors and friends alike with the warmest smile.

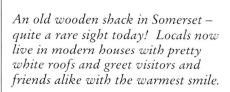

Another entire world survives beneath the roots and grasses, plants and flowers – myriads of insects; their toil is to survive man's powerful sprays and destruction of their habitats.

The Great Egrets are quite common along ponds and farmland.

*The **study** of plants has no boundaries. We all owe it to the world not to destroy our natural heritage.*

PAGET MARSH
Visitors are welcome
to this unspoiled natural area
Please help us to keep it clean.
Trees, plants flowers and earth
may not be taken from the marsh
• BEWARE OF POISON IVY •

Introduction

The Longtails find safe nesting sites along Bermuda's many rocky slopes and cliffs, their majestic flightpath affords a wonderful sight and sound experience. Often in pairs, they fly out from their nests in total harmony with nature, hunting for fish and squid. The Longtails live on the ocean. Their main habitat is the Sargasso Sea which is to the south of Bermuda. Longtails return to the Islands in March, lay their eggs in April and the hatchlings appear in early June. When the chicks leave the nest they fly directly out to sea.

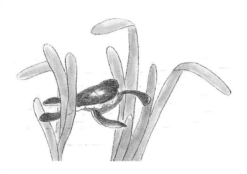

The Green Turtle (found on sea grass)

Sea turtles evolved from a marsh-inhabiting ancestor during Cretaceous times. They are an ancient sub-order of reptiles. The Green Turtle once thrived in Bermuda waters but man hunted them until near extinction. In 1968 a project was started to reintroduce them from the beaches of Costa Rica, with eggs delivered in styrofoam boxes. These eggs were then buried in the sand. After 70 days incubation, the young take seven days to emerge through the sand and make their way to the sea. Few survive the migration of thousands of miles. It is hoped that sometime in the future the turtles will find their way back to Bermuda's beaches and lay their eggs, but as yet this has not occurred.

Other turtles are seen along Bermuda's coastline. The large Leather-Back Turtle roams the surrounding ocean, while the Loggerhead Turtle is sometimes seen close to the shore. The other turtle seen locally is the Hawksbill Turtle, sometimes seen out among the coral reefs (it once provided tortoiseshell).

The bright yellow-breasted Kiskadee was introduced from Trinidad in 1957 to help control the Anolis Lizards that were introduced in 1905.

Sadly, time has shown that this attractive bird created more problems than ever thought possible. It rapidly increased, then became a pest, enjoying the crops of fruit and competing with other birds. The Kiskadee has contributed to the decline in the lovely Vireo and Cardinal populations, also the Catbird.

In springtime you may be fortunate to spot a Humpback Whale pass by. Masters of the ocean, these amazing creatures stir the passion. Sadly their visit is all too short, passing by on their migration – but leaving behind wonderful memories of their sudden but unforgettable sighting.

Spotfin Butterfly Fish
Sergeant-Major

Future generations should have a right to enjoy the carpets of wild flowers. The world has over 250,000 plant species. This is an attempt to bring a few of the dominant species in Bermuda to light.

HAPPY PLANT EXPLORING!

Call us not weeds –
We are flowers of the sea,
For lovely and bright
And gay-tinted are we.
And quite independent
Of sunshine or showers –
Then call us not weeds,
We are the oceans' gay flowers.
Not mussed like the plants
   of a summer pasture –
Whose gales are but sighs
   of an evening air.
Our exquisite, fragile
   and delicate forms,
Are mused by the ocean
And rocked by the storms.

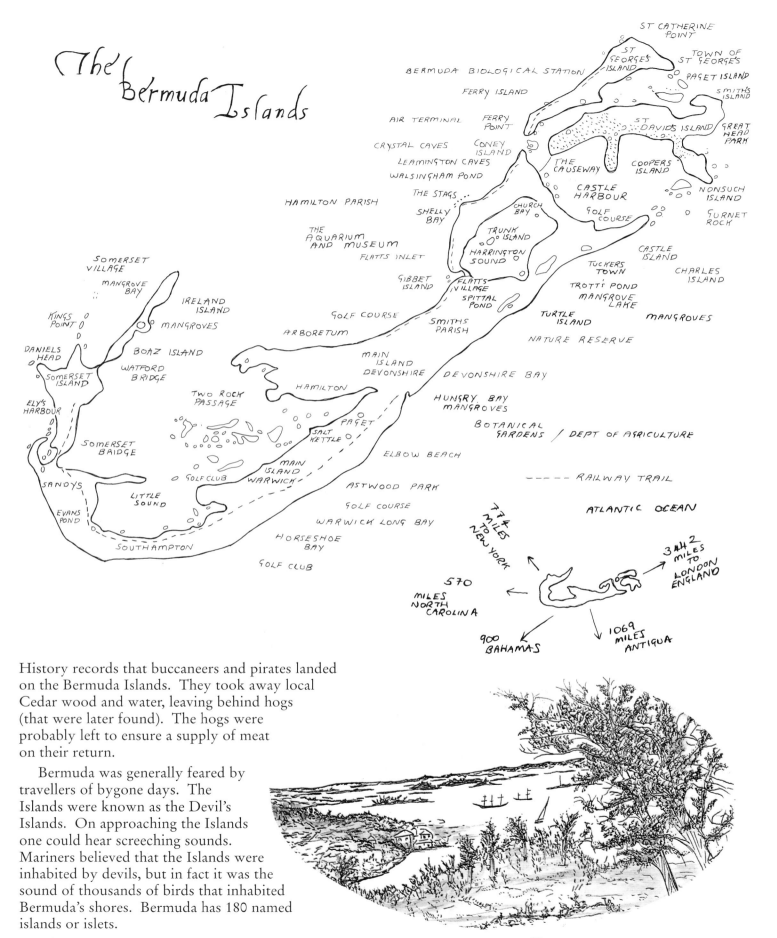

The Bermuda Islands

ST CATHERINE POINT

BERMUDA BIOLOGICAL STATION

ST GEORGES ISLAND

TOWN OF ST GEORGE'S

PAGET ISLAND

SMITHS ISLAND

FERRY ISLAND

AIR TERMINAL

FERRY POINT

ST DAVID'S ISLAND

GREAT HEAD PARK

CRYSTAL CAVES

CONEY ISLAND

COOPERS ISLAND

LEAMINGTON CAVES

THE CAUSEWAY

WALSINGHAM POND

CASTLE HARBOUR

NONSUCH ISLAND

HAMILTON PARISH

THE STAGS

CHURCH BAY

GOLF COURSE

GURNET ROCK

SHELLY BAY

THE AQUARIUM AND MUSEUM

TRUNK ISLAND

CASTLE ISLAND

FLATTS INLET

HARRINGTON SOUND

TUCKERS TOWN

CHARLES ISLAND

SOMERSET VILLAGE

GIBBET ISLAND

FLATTS VILLAGE

TROTT'S POND

MANGROVE BAY

SPITTAL POND

MANGROVE LAKE

IRELAND ISLAND

GOLF COURSE

SMITHS PARISH

TURTLE ISLAND

MANGROVES

KINGS POINT

MANGROVES

ARBORETUM

NATURE RESERVE

DANIELS HEAD

BOAZ ISLAND

MAIN ISLAND DEVONSHIRE

DEVONSHIRE BAY

SOMERSET ISLAND

WATFORD BRIDGE

ELY'S HARBOUR

HAMILTON

HUNGRY BAY MANGROVES

TWO ROCK PASSAGE

BOTANICAL GARDENS / DEPT OF AGRICULTURE

SOMERSET BRIDGE

PAGET

SALT KETTLE

ELBOW BEACH

SANDYS

GOLF CLUB

MAIN ISLAND WARWICK

- - - - - RAILWAY TRAIL

LITTLE SOUND

ASTWOOD PARK

ATLANTIC OCEAN

EVANS POND

GOLF COURSE

774 MILES TO NEW YORK

3442 MILES TO LONDON ENGLAND

SOUTHAMPTON

WARWICK LONG BAY

570 MILES NORTH CAROLINA

HORSESHOE BAY

GOLF CLUB

900 BAHAMAS

1069 MILES ANTIGUA

History records that buccaneers and pirates landed on the Bermuda Islands. They took away local Cedar wood and water, leaving behind hogs (that were later found). The hogs were probably left to ensure a supply of meat on their return.

Bermuda was generally feared by travellers of bygone days. The Islands were known as the Devil's Islands. On approaching the Islands one could hear screeching sounds. Mariners believed that the Islands were inhabited by devils, but in fact it was the sound of thousands of birds that inhabited Bermuda's shores. Bermuda has 180 named islands or islets.

13

2. Bermuda: history and fauna

The passage to the new world of America by the early settlers must have been treacherous. The remnants of the shipwrecks found along the Bermuda reef line are testimony to this. The islands were named in 1510 when a Spanish ship discovered the group of Islands. Its captain, Juan de Bermudez, named the Islands after himself. Then the noted English admiral, Sir George Somers, was shipwrecked in the *Sea Venture* in 1609. He and his party spent ten months there, claiming the Islands for the Crown. During their stay two small ships were built in which they continued their journey to Virginia.

Historical records of A.E. Verrill show the uninhabited Islands of Bermuda to be very rich in plant and bird life. He noted that the hogs roaming the Island were possibly left by the Spanish.

Geographically, Bermuda is situated 570 nautical miles due east of Cape Hatteras, North Carolina, 1000 miles north of Antigua and approximately 3442 miles from London, England. This small and isolated British colony has the most northerly coral reef in the world. As Bermuda's shores are washed with the warm waters of the Gulf Stream, the average temperature is 70° F/21° C. In the summertime the local waters warm up and sub-tropical vegetation thrives on the Islands.

Bermuda is a volcanic sea mountain that rises $2\frac{1}{2}$ miles from the ocean floor, and is part of the mid-Atlantic ridge. The submarine volcano is now covered with a cap of coral reef sediments. Shells off the reef decompose and form the sand; drifting sand made the dune formation and plants arriving by wind, sea or birds created the beginnings of the beach flora which is still evolving.

Bermuda is in fact a group of 180 islands, the five main ones being linked by causeways or bridges. The many other islands are all close together and make a horseshoe shape. The widest point is three miles but the average is about one mile wide. The highest point of Bermuda reaches 259 feet.

Wintry December

The heat of summer gone
A night of wind and rain
Enveloped these tiny islands
Then –
The stillness of morning
With the silvery grey lights
Of the lighthouse beam sea to
land –
The mist envelopes the islands –
Barely in view –
No buildings distinguishable
Just shadows of grey loom
On the horizon; mirrored
On a flat calm sea
To dream perhaps of a
Land untouched by man.

For a brief moment in time
The chaos of this busy little island
World hidden.

A huge rush of tidal change
As if a river flowing below
the still, still sea.

A tiny ripple of a wave
Appears and fades and
Life goes on.

Christine Watlington

The coral reef is breathtaking; enormous caverns with brightly coloured fish, sea fans, coral and anemones dwell in harmony. The depths hold wonders yet to be discovered. The hundreds of ocean and reef-dwelling forms are awe-inspiring, with an unbelievable richness of old shipwrecks.

The Islands today have a very rich flora. Plants from all over the world, both tropical and temperate, grow and thrive on this small landmass of 21 square miles. For example, the Coconuts of the Caribbean add tropical flavour to more familiar friends from the northern temperate regions like the Eucalyptus and Salix (willow). These all thrive in a frost-free climate.

Dense forests of Cedars once covered most of the land, along with palms and other endemic trees.   The first settlers began to use the wood for house building, boat building, furniture and fires. The Bermuda Cedar was the dominant tree until the 1940s when an accidentally introduced scale insect spread through the Island and destroyed most of the trees. Happily the remaining Cedars are holding their own today and replanting schemes implemented in the 1980s are having a wonderfully positive effect. Introduced Agaves also dot the Islands amidst scrubland and Buttonwood. The Casuarina, which now predominates, is a fast-growing pine from Australia, which was introduced to replace the dying Cedars in the late 1940s to help protect the Islands from the high winds.

The northern coastline is very windswept with introduced Tamarisk sheltering the land from winds and salt spray. The southern coastline is much more protected and Hibiscus and Oleander plants thrive there – flowering almost all year round. Just inland from the rocky coastline, salt-marshes link up with deeper inland tidal lakes. Here, large colonies of Black and Red Mangroves thrive and spread.

Soils are predominantly calcareous with occasional sandy pockets or dunes that have formed along the south shore. Valleys contain a rich red, slightly clay soil resulting from leaching of nutrients on the hillsides. In the central valleys one sees an amazing contrast with wet, dark and peaty marshes forming a very specialized ecological niche.

Bermuda has 17 true endemic species surviving and approximately 160 native species. The number of cultivated plants growing on the Island is harder to assess but estimates seem to indicate up to 1300 species with hundreds of cultivars. The reason for this is due to the fact that the Islands have been heavily populated for some time, therefore nurseries introduce new plants because the demand is so great. This book highlights many of these plants, enabling residents and visitors to become better acquainted with Bermuda's botanical wonderland. It is of great importance not to forget that Bermuda still has its own special flora that must be protected. These plants are unique to Bermuda, growing nowhere else and through centuries of isolation have evolved into distinct species from formerly related ones.

Types of flora

ENDEMIC *(17 species in Bermuda)*

An endemic species is a native plant or animal that has been isolated for such a long period of time that it has evolved into its own species. It is only present in that country or locality, making it unique to that area.

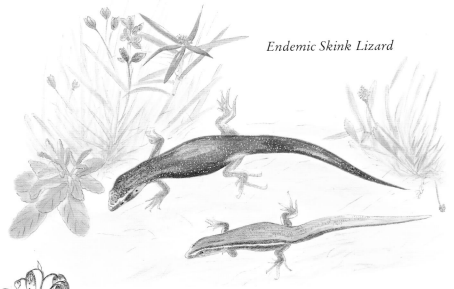

Endemic Skink Lizard

NATIVE *(150 species in Bermuda)*

By definition this is any plant or animal species that occurs naturally in any area, without the aid of man (i.e. indigenous). It also occurs outside Bermuda in the country from whence it came. Everything in this group would have to cross to the Islands by natural means – wind, bird or ocean current. By definition, therefore, everything before man had to be native or endemic.

Tree Frog among Floppers

NATURALIZED *(over 400 species in Bermuda)*

Naturalized plants are ones that man has introduced and which then have become established on their own without man's aid (self-seeding) as if they were native. Any plant can adapt to a new environment and become invasive, given suitable conditions. Fennel is an attractive example.

Agave growing along a hedgerow

INTRODUCED *(1000 species, and growing, in Bermuda)*

These are plants that have been brought to Bermuda by man, unable to come across the ocean or arrive on a bird's wing or by any other means.

Spanish Bayonet along the south shore

EXOTIC *(around 1000 species in Bermuda)*

Exotic plants are those introduced from foreign countries. They are generally strikingly different and unusual.

Bermuda fruits

CULTIVATED *(900 species in Bermuda)*

A cultivated plant is one which has been introduced from its natural habitat, maintained and cultivated in an artificial environment, and is unable to reproduce itself by seed without man's aid.

Flowers in a Bermuda garden

BERMUDA'S 17 ENDEMIC PLANTS

Sadly Bermuda has lost some endemic plants but we hope, with awareness, we can protect the seventeen that are left. The World Conservation Strategy set a policy published in 1980 by UNEP, IUCN, World Wide Fund for Nature to protect wildlife and natural habitats (this is now generally accepted).

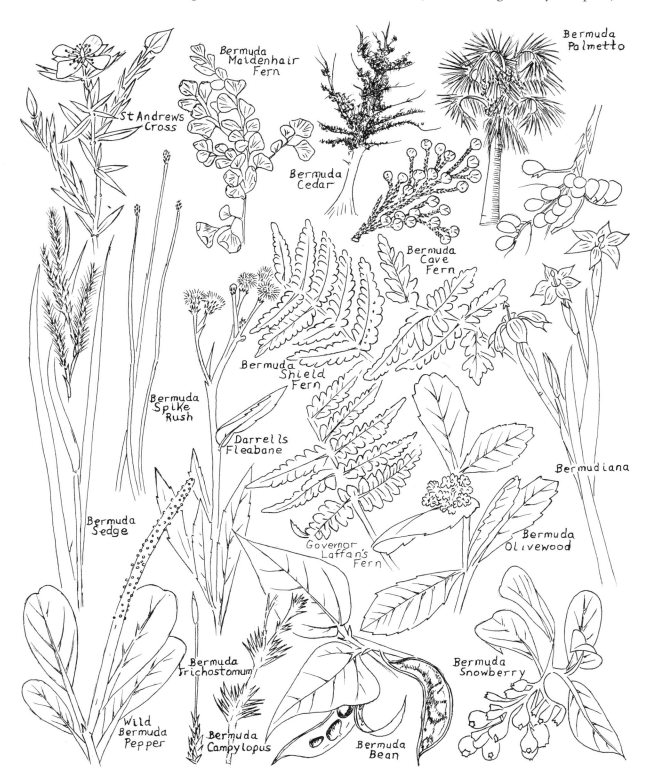

St Andrews Cross

Bermuda Maidenhair Fern

Bermuda Cedar

Bermuda Palmetto

Bermuda Cave Fern

Bermuda Shield Fern

Bermuda Spike Rush

Darrells Fleabane

Bermudiana

Bermuda Sedge

Governor Laffan's Fern

Bermuda Olivewood

Wild Bermuda Pepper

Bermuda Trichostomum

Bermuda Campylopus

Bermuda Bean

Bermuda Snowberry

3. Habitats

SHALLOW SANDY BAYS

Sit for a while and enjoy this wonderful habitat, often bordered by Mangroves, Buttonwood and Sea Ox-Eye. These bays are home to submerged grass-like plants such as Manatee Grass, Sea Grass and Turtle Grass. Keep an eye out for sea turtles, sea birds and herons. Also the Belted Kingfisher, *Magaceryle alcyon*, which migrates from North America, escaping the chilly weather, and sometimes stays into the summer months.

BRACKISH MARSH
(Enclosed and slightly tidal)

Slightly tidal, these inshore ponds, lakes and wetlands have less Mangroves and more open water. Brackish areas easy to see are the Ireland Island Lagoon, Evans Pond, Mangrove Lake and Walsingham Pond. Wildlife is not as rich as coastal Mangrove but look out for Marsh Rosemary, Marsh Samphire, Seaside Heliotrope, Seaside Purslane, Widgeon Grass, Sheathed Paspalum and other naturalized flora (Note plates 7 and 8). Crabs, snails, shell fish, herons, Belted Kingfisher and Pied-Billed Grebe are also found.

COASTAL HILLSIDE AND ROCKS

Coastal hillsides are known as the Land Crab zone. Depending on the height of the cliffs, Longtails find good nesting sites along the rocky foreshore. The native coastal flora tends to have some of the dune plants growing into the rocky slopes, but Sea Ox-Eye, Buttonwood and Coast Spurge are always dominant. Look out also for Bermudiana, Blodgetts Spurge, Bay Bean, Beach Lobelia, Coast Sophora, Coast Spurge, Crab Grass, Cape Weed, Evening Primrose, Darrell's Fleabane, Prickly Pear, Scurvy Grass, Seaside Golden Rod, Salt Grass, Bay Lavender, Seaside Morning Glory, Spanish Bayonet, Tassel Plant, Cedar, Switch Grass, Bay Grape and Jamaica Dogwood.

The south shoreline is so protected that the introduced and exotic plants have found their way there and are doing well in coastal exposures. Bermuda is so very fertile and has perfect weather for most of the year although it does have the occasional hurricane.

MANGROVE SWAMPS - TIDAL LAGOONS

There are many Mangrove swamps, bays and lagoons throughout the Islands. Dense thickets of Mangrove trees are easily seen at Ireland Island lagoon, Mangrove Lake, Evans Pond, Wreck Road and Riddles Bay. Of particular interest are Walsingham and Hungry Bay. Walsingham is a dense swamp of Red Mangrove, *Rhizophora mangle*, with Black Mangrove, *Avicennia nitida*, tending to grow taller. The Red Mangrove has arching stilt roots standing firmly in water and has a fascinating way of reproducing itself. The seed develops into a spear-shaped root which drops into the muddy water below and a new plant forms. Plants and wildlife to look out for are: the Giant Blue Crab, the Giant Toad, the Mangrove Crab, Buttonwood, Salt-Marsh Ox-Eye, Marsh Rosemary, Marsh Samphire, Seaside Heliotrope, Seaside Purslane, Woody Glasswort, and Limonium. The Walsingham swamp borders the Walsingham Jungle.

The other unique area is Hungry Bay swamp, approximately 4000 years old. An old wooden shack built on stilts with a dock is a surprise to see in the middle of this dense seven-acre Mangrove swamp. One imagines being amongst thousands of acres but not so, as the rocky coastline is close by. Look out for the Great Land Crab. The long-term survival of Bermuda's Mangroves could be in jeopardy unless great care is taken to protect them from consequences of modern day pollution such as oil spills.

BEACH AND DUNE

The south shoreline is moulded by the ceaseless energy of the wind and sea which builds the dune, but is equally dependent on the coral reef's protection. Along the dunes and beaches you will find the native coastal flora. The dune habitat interdigiates with the coastal rock habitat but its flora is distinctly different. You will occasionally see the elusive Ghost Crab, Terns and Sandpipers running along the water's edge searching for food. The sun's glare can be so intense that it can be hard to focus on the flowering gems in the sand, or the dramatic blues of the ocean.

Plants to look out for are Beach Lobelia, Beach Croton, Burr Grass, Bermudiana, Bay Grape, Bay Bean, Seashore Rush Grass, Seaside Evening Primrose, Scurvy Grass, Sheathed Paspalum, Seaside Golden Rod, Bay Lavender, Salt Grass, Seaside Morning Glory, Spanish Bayonet, Tassel Plant (Note plates 6,7,39). Introduced plants do find their way into all habitats and at the back of the dunes, on the slopes leading up to the road, Sage Bush, Oleander, Casuarina and Tamarisk mix in with other native and introduced plants, helping to stabilize the dune habitat.

The beauty within the sea and the reef is another world that must not be missed. Coral formations and sea life, brightly-coloured fish, rockfish and lobsters, all live in the reef amongst large, swaying lilac sea fans, truly a painted wonderland, so amazing, it seems unbelievable.

The north shoreline is dramatically different. Weather-beaten gnarled Tamarisk, Buttonwood, Bay Grape and Cedar grow very well, along with many of the other native coastal plants but the force of the weather is felt on this shore and salt-resistant, introduced plants are commonly seen. Casuarina, Oleander and Pittosporum, Screw Palm, and also Wedelia are commonly planted as they stand up to salt spray. Also seen a lot is Fennel, Golden Rod and Asparagus Fern. The fierce winter winds from the north send great sea waves crashing over the shoreline and occasionally one can see the giant ocean swell being stopped by the north reef on the horizon.

UPLAND HILLSIDES

The original forest consisted mainly of three endemic trees, the Bermuda Cedar, the Palmetto and Bermuda Olivewood. Today introduced plants are dominant and most areas have lost their original appearance. Most woodland flora vary from one area to another, depending on soil types and location. It is quite common today to see woodlands of Spice, Cherry and Fiddlewood with Mexican Pepper mixed in. The Devonshire Marsh woodland is typical of the secondary forest and includes the plants mentioned above.

The Walsingham Jungle is similar but much more of the original flora is found, due to large clearings of controlled conservation projects keeping original flora alive. Conspicuous plants seen are Palmetto, Cedar, Wild Indigo, Lamarcks Trema, Olivewood, Burr Bush, Snowberry, Sword Fern, Jasmine Vine, Maurandia Vine and Buddleia. Gilbert Hill, sloping down to the south shore, has much Forestiera growing. Paynters Hill has some of the rarer plants and much of the original flora (but can only be seen on a guided tour). Abbotts Cliff has a good stand of Southern Hackberry. There is a lovely walk down to the Mussel Man's Beach, a little beach where fishermen of Harrington Sound sort out their catch of mussels, leaving thousands of shells behind.

Other plants to look out for are Balloon Vine, Bermuda Bean, Briar Bush, Bracken, Bermuda Bedstraw, Blodgetts Spurge, Cape Weed, Crab Grass, Cyperus, Doc Bush, Jamaica Dogwood, Joseph's Coat, Rhacoma, Shrubby Fleabane, Turnera, White Stopper, Wild Coffee, Virginia Creeper and Wood Grass.

UPLAND VALLEY

This is the most modified habitat. There are no surviving examples of original forest here as the habitat was totally cleared for agriculture soon after settlement. Some efforts are being made to recreate this habitat on Nonsuch Island and in Walsingham. Some of these areas are managed and protected to cull out invading plants, while some are not (having many introduced plants drifting into this habitat). Many upland habitats are part of a programme to recreate the original flora. This is an ongoing programme that is islandwide.

Some native and endemic plants to look out for are Bermuda Cedar, Briar Bush, Bermuda Bean, Bear's Foot, Black Nightshade, Bird Pepper, Balloon Vine, Cape Weed, Crab Grass, Darell's Fleabane, Jamaica Dogwood, Jamaica Weed, Joseph's Coat, Jamaica Vervain, Paspalums, Poison Ivy, Purple Morning Glory, Rhacoma, Snowberry, Southern Hackberry, Sword Fern, Sage Bush, Wild Coffee, Virginia Creeper, Wood Grass and Yellow Wood.

Introduced plants, dominated by Cherry, Spice, Fiddlewood and Mexican Pepper, are very invasive. Birds are the main carriers of seed. Introduced garden plants have spread and adapted to wild locations, occurring in and crossing different habitats so successfully that it is difficult to distinguish them from native plants (because Bermuda's climate is so agreeable for them).

FRESHWATER WETLAND, PONDS AND MARSHES

Freshwater marshland with peat (acid soil) is still dominated by native and endemic marsh flora. Some areas are richer than others, lush habitats for plants, birds and fish. Herons, Egrets and Ducks almost seem tame. Devonshire Marsh, Spittal Pond, Long Bay Pond, Seymours Pond, Warwick and Nonsuch Ponds are particularly special. Look out for Cattail, The Great American Bullrush, Paspalum, Eclipta, Water Smartweed and Knotted Spike Rush.

Devonshire's wetlands are densely vegetated and house several species of Marsh ferns, green hues of every description touching from one branch to another. Giant Ferns mixed in with Wax Myrtle, Doc Bush, Cedar and Palmetto are the most conspicuous plants seen. Some freshwater plants grow almost totally submerged while others have their roots firmly planted on the water's edge.

Paget Marsh is a unique area surrounded by a protective Spice tree woodland. The man-made freshwater ditch is filled with rushes, grasses and a mix of other lovely marshland plants. It is much the same as when the first settlers arrived, with dense Palmetto and Cedar, Wax Myrtle and other native plants making a perfect canopy for the rich fern growth below. Other plants to look out for are Cinnamon Fern, Bermuda Sedge, Bracken, Marsh Shield Fern, Royal Fern, Sword Fern, Virginia Chain Fern, Day Flower, Doc Bush, Duckweed, Eclipta, Mermaid Weed, Ditchweed, Pennywort, Psilotum, Spike Rush, Smartweed, St Andrew's Cross, Turkey Berry, Virginia Creeper, White-Headed Rush and Wood Grass.

In Paget Marsh two exotics were invading the area – Ardisia and Guava. Measures have been taken by the conservation team to control them. It is wise to take a tour or go with someone familiar with this area, as it is easy to get lost amidst Poison Ivy, *Rhus radicans.*

ARABLE LAND AND MEADOWS

Although in the past decades much arable land was built on, today most of the fertile pockets are farmed. There are citrus and banana plantations and a great diversity of other fruits and vegetables. Bermuda could almost be self-sufficient with many crops such as lettuce, tomatoes, potatoes, carrots, pumpkin, water melon, etc. that do very well. It is fair to say that most edible crops have been tried at some point. During the nineteenth century Bermuda was famous for its onions as well as tobacco, corn, cassava and arrowroot which were exported. Easter Lily plantations also once provided Bermuda with a major export crop. Sadly a virus disease destroyed many of the bulbs. Resistant bulbs still provide good crops locally and flowers can be found popping up in all sorts of places. Every spring Easter Lilies are selected and sent to H.M. Queen Elizabeth in London.

When in the depth of farmland and meadows, one can almost forget that habitation is close by. In the early spring and summer, field edges provide good wild flower habitats. One can pray it will stay that way as they are an important habitat for wild flowers, insects and birds. Occasionally you will see a field of red, yellow and lilac poppies when a farmer has allowed a field to go wild after he has harvested a crop.

GARDENS

Because of Bermuda's favourable climate, a vast range of trees, shrubs and herbs from all corners of the world are found in local gardens. There are totally wild gardens as well as formal gardens in some of the most romantic settings imaginable. Many Bermuda gardens are fortunate enough to have native plants growing naturally in them, and as awareness of conservation grows, it has become more popular for local nurseries to grow native plants along with the wealth of temperate and tropical plants that they import. There are a number of groups, such as the Garden Club, the Orchid Society, and the Rose Society, that provide expert information on plants and propagation.

Plants are grown for various reasons, sometimes for the pure love of the plants, or perhaps to encourage birds and butterflies (i.e. the Ink Berry and Milkweed). Interest in gardening and plants often comes along if you want to screen one property from another, or simply plant to beautify your environment. The age-old hobby of exchanging plants thrives in Bermuda, especially through the Garden Club, where at each meeting members bring along their extra plants, bulbs, fruit, etc., for a plant exchange.

Lovely wild plants appear in grasslands in most Bermuda gardens and if not mown in the winter, the early spring will bring Freesias, Oxalis, Nasturtiums, Star of the Veldt and Asters. Atamasco Lilies come a little later, as do the mass of wild grasses, and the Bermudiana. Herbs are very popular, both wild and cultivated and are used locally for culinary and medicinal purposes. An amazing summer sight is the Wild Fennel, which grows along roadsides and hedgerows and can be up to 7 feet high. Many exotic plants thrive in secluded, private settings, such as the Sacred Lotus Flower 'Nelumbo' at Sea Garden in Somerset. Although attractive, the very invasive 'Elephant Ear' can take over a garden, smothering other plants and climbing up trees by means of its aerial roots. A large garden at Southlands along the south shore has a massive Ban Yan tree that covers almost an acre of land. Large Ficus trees appear in many gardens. The rose has a special place in most gardens. Roses were brought into Bermuda by the early settlers.

The Garden Club's 'House and Garden' tour is a must in the spring. The Bermuda Botanical Garden is very well kept and has a wonderful collection of ferns, orchids, cacti, etc. Also Fort Hamilton and Hamilton Parks have good collections of plants. Not to be forgotten are the wonderful National Trust properties and the Aquarium which has recreated the undersea world in giant tanks along with exotic birds and other zoo animals all living within a wonderful plant environment. The hotels and guest houses have wonderful cultivated gardens and Government House has a magnificent garden. Bermuda is kept very clean and tidy, indeed, one could say that Bermuda is rather like a large, immaculately kept garden.

Sacred Lotus Flower 'Nelumbo'

LIMESTONE SINKS

These areas of limestone terrain are characterized by sinks, underground caves and pinnacle rock, with pockets of alkaline clay soils. They are technically known as karsts. The flora appears rich, but in fact many of the rare plants are in danger.

Walsingham is a typical karst area. A few yards from the lovely old Tom Moore's Tavern, is a path into a rare Bermuda jungle. The path through the dense invasive Cherry trees is bordered by Red and Black Mangrove trees on one side and a woodland, leading to the coast, on the other. The path leads to a clearing where a solitary Palmetto stands to your left and beyond that, the remains of the old Calabash tree where Tom Moore, the poet, wrote many a verse. This clearing has many interesting plants, including Bermuda Olivewood, Roving Sailor Vine, Buddleia and Floppers growing wild amidst all the native and endemic flora. To the right is a rocky tidal pool (surrounded by vegetation) which often has fish swimming in the currents. Up higher, into the Cherry thicket, you may note Jasmine Vine. The patch will lead you to underground caves.

Within the many sinks in this area, a conservation team is culling out invasive plants, thus recreating areas of Bermuda's original forest by keeping only native and endemic plants. This is not an easy task when surrounded by invasive introduced plants. These ongoing projects will ensure native plants are protected.

Plants to look out for are Burr Bush, Balloon Vine, Briar Bush, Bermuda Bean, Doc Bush, Ferns, Foresteria, Joseph's Coat, Jamaica Dogwood, Lamarcks Trema, Turkey Berry, Turnera, Slender Paspalum, Shrubby Fleabane, Virgate Mimosa, Virginia Creeper, Wax Myrtle, Yellow Wood, Olivewood, Palmetto, Bermuda Cedar. Many other native and introduced plants can be seen in plates 1, 2, 3, 4, 5, 8 and 23.

HEDGEROW, WAYSIDE AND ROCKY OUTCROPS

Bermuda has approximately 130 miles of roads bordered by hedgerows, which provide one of the biggest habitats for wild flowers. Native and endemic flora are mixed in with naturalized and exotic trees, shrubs wild plants and vines. Hedgerows of Hibiscus, Match-Me-If-You-Can and Oleander are commonly seen. Mixed in with masses of wild heath are dense Bamboo thickets, Queen Anne's Lace, exotic Aloes and Agaves, Cactus plants and wild herbs, forming a unique mix of plant life to rival any in the world.

Tropical trees tower above, including Poinciana, African Tulip tree, Norfolk Island Pine, Casuarina and many palms. Many of the plants you see within these pages can often be seen growing in limestone which has stood the test of time.

Corners of tumbling Nasturtium and Bermudiana grow together, hoping to escape the indiscriminate use of cutting and spraying machines. Grass verges and waysides should not be cut until the wild plants have had time to seed. Wild flowers provide a home and refuge for many birds and insects all needing to survive. The flowers die back towards the end of June when the temperature rises and soon thereafter the seeds set. The eager strimmer should wait until this time before tidying his hedgerow, allowing nature to fulfil its intended path.

Other plants to look out for are Darrell's Fleabane, Turnera, Joseph's Coat, Cape Weed, Mimosa, Snowberry, Sword Fern, Creeping Fern, Fennel, Beggar's Ticks Grasses, Ivy, Maurandya Vines, Moss, Asparagus Ferns, Cherry, Mexican Pepper, Ruselia Heath, Cow Parsley, Horse Weeds, Mustard, etc. (see plates 9,11,12,13 and 14).

Ground Doves: If you are as quiet as a mouse you might see a pair of Ground Doves nibbling at seeds. At the slightest noise they flutter off in a second. Often seen on pathways close to cultivated ground.

ISLANDS

Along the quiet coastal stretches and on little islands, one finds peace and harmony with nature, totally unspoiled areas taking care of themselves. Herons and many seabirds, such as Gulls, Terns, Plovers and Sandpipers, are secure in this habitat. Crabs and a myriad of other creatures dart over and under rock formations.

Many native plants seen growing on Bermuda today were originally from seeds carried here by ocean currents, from the West Indies or North America. Nonsuch Island is the jewel in Bermuda's crown of islands and there is much to study and learn within its 15 acres of land, just a short boat ride from the mainland. Only 30 years ago it was a desolate, windblown island, but today it has the reputation of being one of the world's most fascinating conservation projects, largely due to one dedicated man, Dr David Wingate who is the Bermuda Government Conservation Officer, and his team of conservationists and helpers.

On approaching the island, one might think that few plants would survive there. The cliffs are exposed and windblown but, remarkably, the weather-beaten vegetation holds on throughout the toughest climatic conditions, protecting the inner sanctum from fierce, salt-laden winds. A rusty old ship-wreck has been placed on the north side of the island, making a sheltered area, so landing is possible. On walking up the steep steps, one reaches the old house and the character of the island begins to unfold. Sepia photographs displayed in the house depict the island's history and ongoing projects. Also, there is a picture of Dr William Bebe, a dedicated naturalist, working on the island.

Looking out to the south of the island from the old veranda, there is the most breathtaking view of the chain of the Castle Islands. When scanning the horizon through the old telescope that is positioned on the veranda, you may be lucky enough to see the migration of the Shearwater birds or the Humpback Whale, if you are there at the right time of year. The old house, once home to yellow fever victims, is today used by visiting scientists and students. Committed to natural history, they come to study the many aspects of Bermuda's wildlife and help with ongoing projects.

Of great interest is the work concerning two birds. First the Longtail that you will see in the spring and summer. They come to the Islands to breed and they make their nests in the rockface. David Wingate has helped with their survival by making burrows in safe nesting sites. The other bird project is the protection of the rare Cahow, once thought to be extinct but now surviving with about 50 breeding pairs. This bird, which has attracted international interest since the early 1900s when it was first re-sighted, was once so plentiful that it was an important food for the early settlers. In 1951, David Wingate and his group made the exciting discovery that confirmed that the Cahow still exists and for the past 40 years he has dedicated himself to their survival.

Today, Nonsuch Island is lush and overgrown with the original mainland habitats re-created, including a freshwater marsh, Cedar and Palmetto thickets and an abundance of native and endemic flora. The rare Skink Lizard happily survives and birds and butterflies are plentiful, particularly the Monarch, the Bermuda Buckeye and the Gulf Fritillary, all living in paradise with plants such as the tiny Ink Berry.

One can only hope that man will protect this special island and its plants and wildlife for time immemorial.

4. Making the most of this book

The objective of this book is to provide a comprehensive, yet easy to understand guide to the identification of the plants in Bermuda. I have compiled it to fill a void in literature so that anyone, amateur or professional, visitors, residents or students, may, at a glance, have reference to the identification of the colourful and diverse range of plants found on these Islands.

Everyone develops different methods of identifying plants. One usually notes a combination of characteristics that may be recognizable from a distance, the habit or form, or a certain type of bark. Others may require closer examination or study of a flower, fruit, leaf or twig.

By taking time to walk along roadsides, beaches, tribe roads, nature reserves – hill and dale, you will be continually confronted with abounding beauty. Using all the plant characteristics, including leaf variations, smell and touch, you will soon acquire a basic botanical knowledge. It is a satisfying and gratifying way of communicating with nature and the environment.

Endangered or rare plants must be totally respected. Picking them may cause their destruction, and is illegal. All characteristics described are those which can easily be seen, thus avoiding the need to pick or remove the plants from their habitats. Never tamper with plants, they cannot protect themselves, and many species have already been lost to science, so always leave plants in their habitats for others to enjoy. Remember, when you pick a flower you stop it reproducing, seeding and spreading. Always take a book to the plant and not the plant to the book.

It is helpful to take a small notebook and a pencil when out looking at plants. This will enable you to make simple sketches of flowers, leaves or fruit. Things to note for identification are: arrangement of flowers; size, shape, colour of flower fruit or seed; type of habitat, whether common or infrequent; if woody, herbaceous, or other.

Plants and their common names vary from place to place, but botanists and zoologists are able to communicate using Latin. Latin has long been used as a universal scientific language. To simplify learning, the technical information and terms are kept to a minimum – each plant described has an illustration next to its text. Where appropriate, notes on local use and plant locations are given.

The index is arranged in two sections, the first starting with the Latin botanical names, and the second starting with the English names. The numbers refer to the plates.

Botanists change plant names from time to time, so one cannot hope for all the names to be updated. Most botanical books have some naming problems. I have spent much time over the years checking names in plant books and dictionaries. My final list was further updated by two plantsmen who made some changes and I can be sure, as far as possible, that this represents a good list for the 1990s. I hope it will be helpful.

EXPLORE SEASHORE TO HILLSIDE

Along the seashore look closely for the Sargasso seaweed and also sea grasses. You may see the occasional Portuguese Man-O-War or the Ghost Crabs with their iridescent look. Then further inland the orange and brown Land Crabs and their burrows can be seen. The ocean affords movement and change each day so watch closely for the many fish that populate the shallows. Look out also for the white-flowered Scurvy Grass. This plant was invaluable to the sailors of yesteryear, to aid recovery from the ailment after which it is named.

Sandy pockets among the rocks are full of Sea Ox-Eye with its green and glaucous leaves and stiff yellow daisy-like flowers. Sandpipers rushing in and out of the waves are a joy to watch. From spring to autumn the Longtails display their flying techniques with amazing agility. As you walk along the beach try to identify the coastal plants. Study the rock formations; you may be lucky to see a fossil of a plant or creature.

Some plants open at sunrise others wait until dusk, notably the lovely beach Evening Primrose with yellow flowers turning to orange. In April or May you will find the national flower, Bermudiana. Never be tempted to pick its tiny purple-blue flowers; remember plants need their seed to reproduce for the next generation.

The Spanish Bayonet (Yucca) dot the sand dunes with great spikes of white flowers. Inland you will find brackish swampy areas and small lagoons filled with Mangroves along with an abundance of salt-water plants. Mangroves have evergreen foliage, and a root network which creates an ideal sheltered environment for Herons and Giant Blue Crabs. Hungry Bay is quite the nicest place to study this type of environment. On a sunny day the peace and calm of the bay and the filtered light give a true experience of paradise found.

In Devonshire Marsh, now excavated for better drainage and to hold fish for mosquito control, you will notice open fields and man-made ditches, once used for celery growing. The water close to the road looks like a natural stream and has giant ferns on its banks. The occasional Wax Myrtle trees grow almost as high as the Palmetto and Bermuda Cedar trees. Within the marsh, the Doc Bush seems to thrive and survive well with its feet in water.

On the northern side of the road a colourful and well forested hillside of Fiddlewood and Allspice grow in harmony, together with Wild Sage bush. Beware of Poison Ivy as this habitat is ideal for its rampant growth. Poison Ivy plants tumble freely over shrubs and trees.

Occasionally one can find interesting things to take home or to school for others to enjoy and identify – shells, dried seed heads, discarded crab shells, or floating *objets d'art* that drift amidst the oceans of the world, and find themselves on Bermuda's beaches. You might study a tiny sample of the sea's flowers – seaweed or Sargasso Weed commonly seen coming and going with the varying tidal conditions.

In the spring and summer look out for grasses – Briza grass is one of my favourites. It is like the grasslands' Chandelier waiting for the dance of the fairies at dusk. With so much to see why not sketch or take your camera with you to capture some of nature's wonders – such pleasure can be found just sitting quite still and listening to the birds and tree frogs. Now venture into the caves and deep sinks to experience more wonders from the formation of stalagmites and stalactites to the rich fern growth and roots of the Jasmine Vine. Walsingham and Abbot's Cliff are the finest places to experience this dense upland hillside habitat at the eastern end of Bermuda. Paget Marsh, with its rich Palmetto forest and lush fern growth, sits quite still and undisturbed amidst a hectic bustling urban area. The marsh promises an amazing experience as you walk through the giant ferns and then crunch over fallen palm leaves. The colours within provide lovely subtle shades as shafts of sunlight filter through. The rare St Andrew's Cross and *Carex bermudiana* can be seen, along with the wiry stems of *Psilotum nudum* and the Wood Grass.

Nonsuch Island, the gem of hope that began the real awareness of conservation in Bermuda, may only be visited with a permit and guide. Nonsuch has the strength ... hope ... excitement and beauty of all the best in Bermuda in one tiny area of an Island. Nonsuch – a place where many come, but can we learn to understand its total dignity ...?

5. The Plates

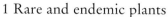

Bermudiana

Sisyrinchium bermudiana   Iridaceae

Endemic, often referred to as the National Flower, common on grassy and sandy hillsides and many inland gardens and walls. Flowers from April to June. Abundant seed which germinates the following year. Thrives along the south shore sand dune areas. Flowers purple, seen islandwide. History tells of Bermudiana covering almost every inch of land and thought of as a pest plant. Now considered a delightful wild flower.

Bermuda Bean

Phaseolus lignosus   Leguminosae

A climbing, scrambling vine with pea-like flowers localized in three areas of Walsingham Cave district. Government has an endangered plant propagation programme where young plants have been grown and reintroduced into the wild. It was recorded that given the correct conditions it grew as well as the common Morning Glory. Flowers yellow to blue.

Turnera West Indian Holly

Turnera ulmifolia   Turneraceae

Native, widespread but uncommon and localized, particularly on dry, shrubby hillsides, road-cuts and path edges.

Turkey Berry

Callicarpa americana   Verbenaceae

A rare native plant that used to be quite common in woodlands; possibly other invading plants took its place. With culling out of the invading plants, Turkey Berry has begun to take hold again on managed nature reserves. A shrub with many pink flowers in cymes, rounded ovate leaves and purple fruits.

Psilotum

Psilotum nudum   Psilotaceae

Native, common in Paget Marsh under Palmettos. Extremely rare and localized in Walsingham Cave district and other upland sites.

Wild Bermuda Pepper

Peperomia septentrionalis   Piperaceae

Endemic. Uncommon and localized on shady mossy rocks in Walsingham Cave district. Rare in Paget Marsh. Flowers minute on slender spikes. Abundant in Castle Harbour area.

Bermuda Campylopus (moss)

Campylopus bermudianus   Dicranaceae

Endemic. Very rare. Seen around the base of Palmetto trees in Paget Marsh only.

Briar Bush

Caesalpinia crista   Leguminosae

Native, extremely rare and localized in a few sites in Devonshire, Smiths, Hamilton and Somerset parishes. A large rambling vine with recurved thorns on every leaf and pod. Flowers yellow. Endangered.

Rattle Box

Crotalaria spectabilis   Leguminosae

Native, very rare. Yellow flowers seen in the autumn. A healthy plant can be seen in the Walsingham Cave district.

Bermuda Bedstraw

Galium bermudense   Rubiaceae

Native. Rare on grassy hillsides, declining rapidly. Has square stems covered in stipules and has unmistakable whorled leaves, tiny white flowers and blue-grey fruits.

Darrell's Fleabane

Erigeron darrellianus   Compositae

Endemic, found occasionally along sandy coastal embankments. Tiny clusters of daisy-like flowers seen from March. Makes a lovely garden plant when seed can be found.

Bermuda Spike Rush

Eleocharis bermudiana   Cyperaceae

Endemic. Extremely rare, found on the edge of shaded pools in peat marshes of Devonshire and Paget Marshes. Endangered.

Bermuda Trichostomum (moss)

Trichostomum bermudanum   Pottiaceae

Endemic. The common moss that can be found along most walls and damp, shaded bare ground.

A traveller should be a botanist, for in all views plants form the chief embellishment.

Charles Darwin

RARE AND ENDEMIC PLANTS
Plate 1

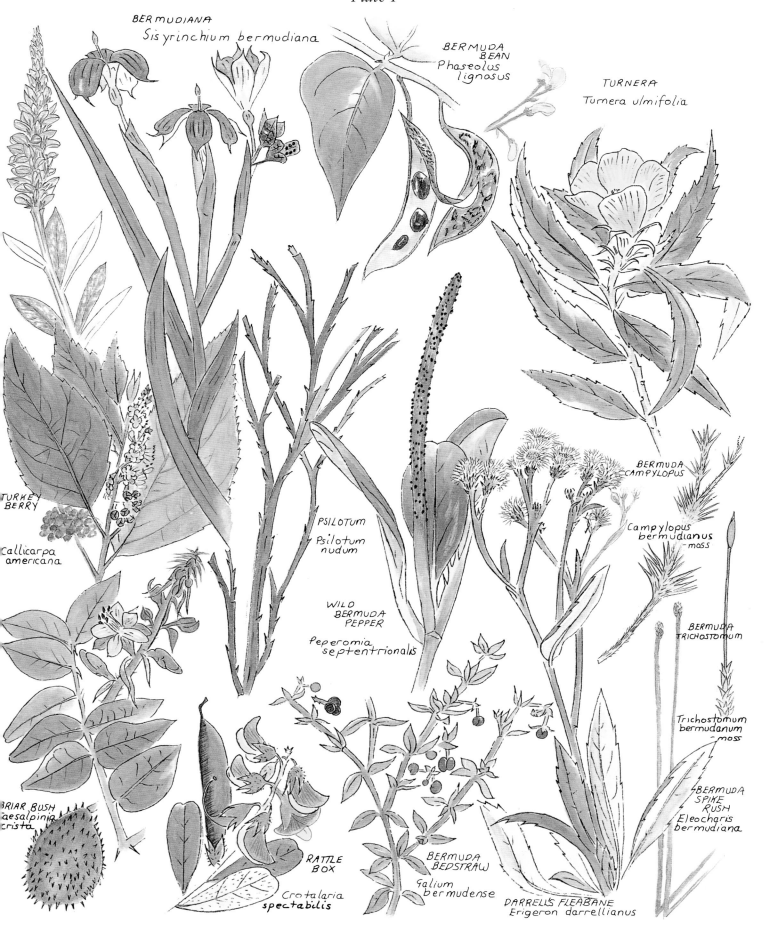

BERMUDIANA
Sisyrinchium bermudiana

BERMUDA BEAN
Phaseolus lignosus

TURNERA
Turnera ulmifolia

TURKEY BERRY
Callicarpa americana

PSILOTUM
Psilotum nudum

WILD BERMUDA PEPPER
Peperomia septentrionalis

BERMUDA CAMPYLOPUS
Campylopus bermudianus -moss

BERMUDA TRICHOSTOMUM

Trichostomum bermudanum -moss

BERMUDA SPIKE RUSH
Eleocharis bermudiana

BRIAR BUSH
Caesalpinia crista

RATTLE BOX
Crotalaria spectabilis

BERMUDA BEDSTRAW
Galium bermudense

DARRELL'S FLEABANE
Erigeron darrellianus

Bermuda Cedar (Bermuda Juniper)

Juniperus bermudiana   Cupressaceae

Endemic, evergreen tree growing up to 40 feet high. Once the dominant forest tree of Bermuda. Decimated by Cedar scale insect epidemic in the 1940s. Now not as common but seen all over upland, coastal and peat marsh habitats and seems to be recovering, with and without human aid. I have noted fresh growth on trees thought to be dying.

Bay Grape

Coccoloba uvifera   Polygonaceae

A sprawling, semi-deciduous tree up to 30 feet in height. Common in its native range between Warwick and Devonshire on the south shore. Also grows elsewhere in coastal and upland areas. Sometimes planted in parks and gardens. Dry season deciduous, the shiny, round leaves turning bright reds, oranges and yellows before shedding in April. New leaves are brown turning to bright green with red veins.

Buttonwood

Conocarpus erectus   Combretaceae

At times prostrate, to sprawling shrub or low-growing tree from 5 to 20 feet high. Widespread and common on rocky coastal habitats, especially on sheltered harbour shores.

Red Mangrove

Rhizophora mangle   Rhizophoraceae

Originally from Florida, the West Indies and South America. Common along muddy, sheltered shorelines, producing many trunks and stilt roots accumulating into dense thickets. Long-stemmed yellow flowers with hairy, red lobes inside. Usually reproduces by the seed germinating on the tree, then dropping into the soil and self-rooting.

Black Mangrove

Avicennia nitida   Verbenaceae

Evergreen tree up to 30 feet high. Widespread and common in sediment-filled coastal bays. Normally seen growing amidst the Red Mangrove trees. Often grows 3-4 feet taller.

Here in the stillness
The sea breathes low,
and the high stars
wake in the sky.
For is it not true
that the wonder is
lost in childhood?

- Alfred Noyes

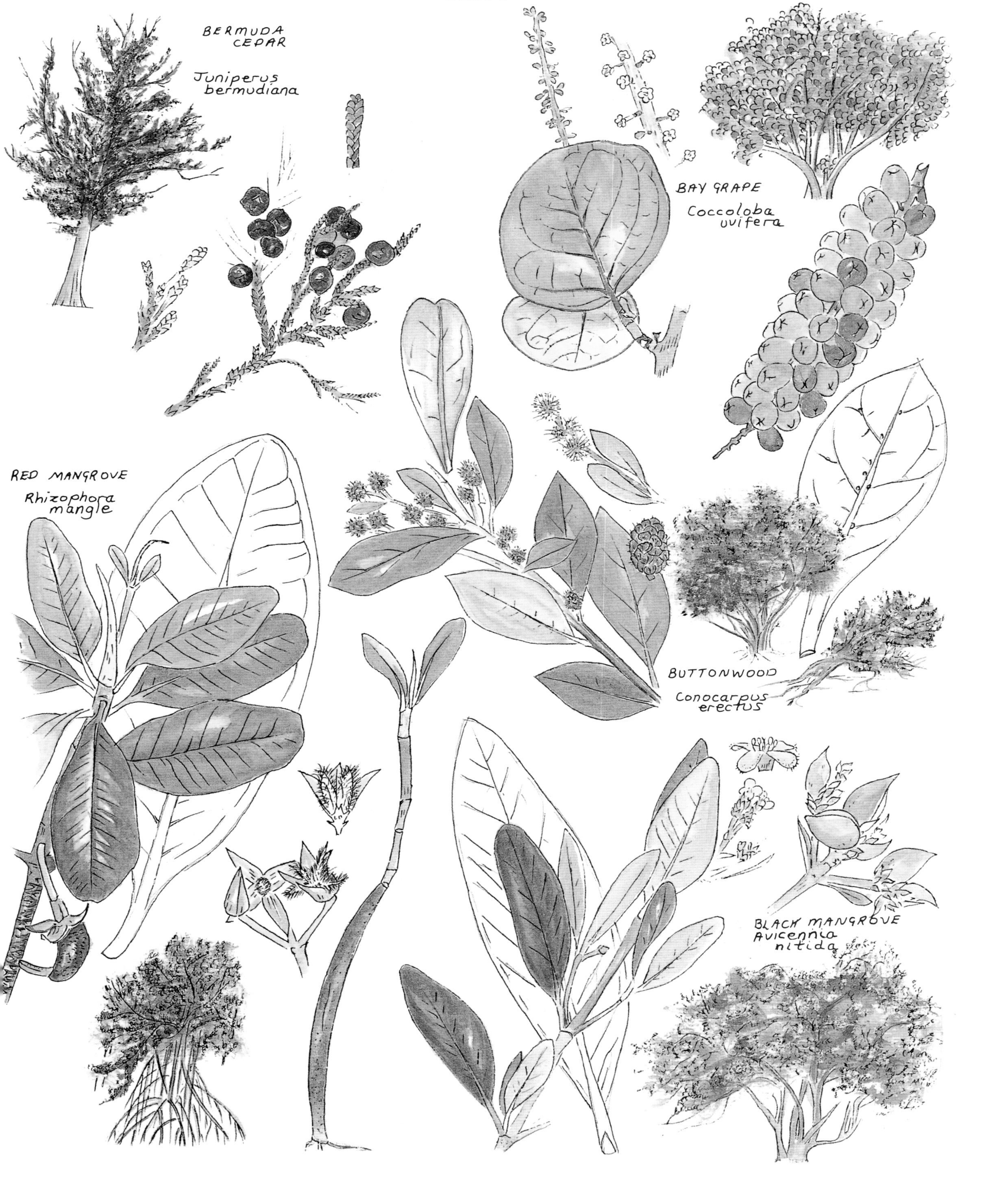

BERMUDA
CEDAR

*Juniperus
bermudiana*

BAY GRAPE
*Coccoloba
uvifera*

RED MANGROVE

*Rhizophora
mangle*

BUTTONWOOD

*Conocarpus
erectus*

BLACK MANGROVE
*Avicennia
nitida*

Southern Hackberry

Celtis laevigata   Ulmacea

A winter deciduous tree growing up to 40 feet high. Uncommon, found in Walsingham Cave district. Very rare in isolated pockets elsewhere on Bermuda in upland habitat. The flush of new leaves in late March is very beautiful.

Yellow Wood

Zanthoxylum flavum   Rutaceae

Semi-deciduous tree 15-20 feet high. Very rare, at two isolated localities. Endangered. Flowers tiny, creamy-white, followed by distinctive black seeds.

Bermuda Olivewood

Cassine laneana   Celastraceae
(syn. *Elaeodendron laneanum*)

Endemic, evergreen tree, slow growing up to 25-40 feet. Formerly uncommon and localized to Walsingham Cave area. Now quite widely planted in gardens. The early settlers used its bark for tanning, this would be the most likely reason that it is not as common now as it once was. A very dense foliaged tree, the new pale green leaves look beautiful against the older dark green foliage.

Forestiera

Forestiera segregata (laneanum)   Oleaceae

Semi-deciduous shrub or small tree growing up to 15 feet high. Widespread but localized in undisturbed upland habitats, especially in Walsingham and on Cooper's Island.

The breath of Nature and her endless bloom.

Plate 3

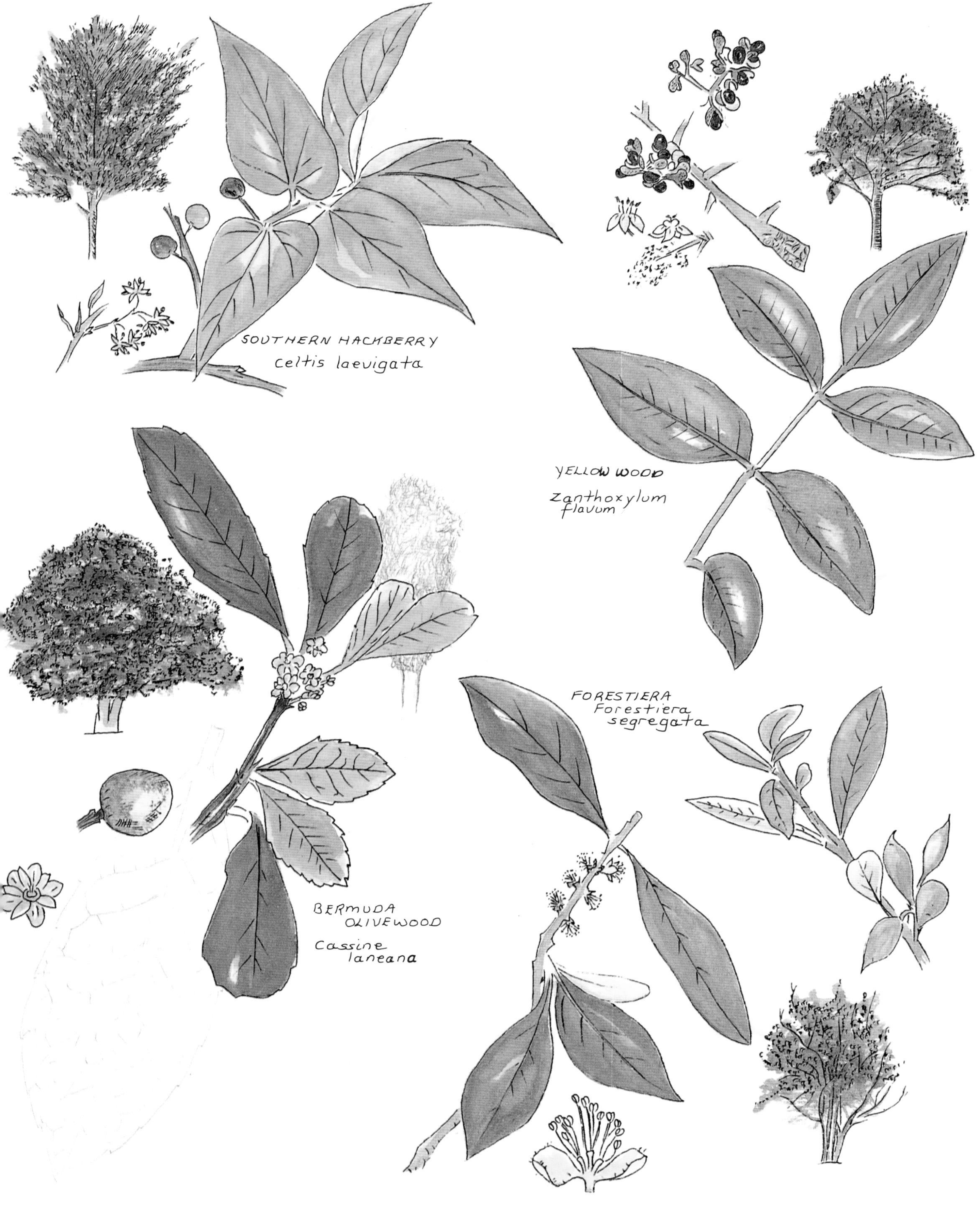
SOUTHERN HACKBERRY
Celtis laevigata
YELLOW WOOD
Zanthoxylum flavum
BERMUDA OLIVEWOOD
Cassine laneana
FORESTIERA
Forestiera segregata

4 Native and endemic shrubs

Bermuda Snowberry

Chiococca bermudiana   Rubiaceae

Widespread but generally uncommon in undisturbed upland habitats, in Walsingham Cave district only. It is becoming a popular garden plant mainly for its showy snow-white fruits.

Jamaica Dogwood

Dodonaea viscosa   Sapindaceae

Widespread and sometimes common, but localized in undisturbed upland habitats, especially on sandy soils.

Shrubby Fleabane

Pluchea odorata   Compositae

An evergreen shrub up to 8-10 feet high. Widespread in upland and peat marsh habitats, quickly invading cleared areas. Devonshire Marsh area has a healthy stand.

Box Briar

Randia aculeata   Rubiaceae

An evergreen shrub growing up to 5 feet high. Uncommon and localized in sandy upland habitats, in Paget and Warwick parishes.

White Stopper

Eugenia monticola (syn. *Eugenia axillaris*)   Myrtaceae

An evergreen shrub or small tree growing up to 15 feet. Widespread but localized in undisturbed upland habitats, especially the Walsingham Cave district. Regularly attacked by leaf-miner caterpillar.

Wild Coffee Shrub

Psychotria undata   Rubiaceae

A rare shrub growing up to 8 feet high. Found in rocky woodlands in the Castle Harbour area. A native plant, flowering in the spring followed by bright red fruits.

Lamarcks Trema

Trema lamarckiana   Ulmaceae

A sprawling, evergreen shrub or small tree 5-15 feet high. Rare and localized in Walsingham Cave district only. Endangered. A distant relative of the Elm tree.

All things bright and
beautiful
All creatures great and small
All things wise and
wonderful
The Lord God made
them all.

BERMUDA SNOWBERRY
Chiococca bermudiana

JAMAICA DOGWOOD
Dodonaea viscosa

SHRUBBY FLEABANE
Pluchea odorata

BOX BRIAR
Randia aculeata

WHITE STOPPER
Eugenia monticola

WILD COFFEE SHRUB
Psychotria undata

LAMARCKS TREMA
Trema lamarckiana

Tassel Plant
Suriana maritima   Surianaceae
Sprawling, evergreen fleshy-leaved shrub 5-10 feet high. Fairly common but localized in rocky coastal and beach habitats.

Spanish Bayonet
Yucca aloifolia   Agavaceae
The sword-like foliage of this plant is very sharp, great care must be taken. The cream flowers appear throughout the summer. Commonly seen along dunes and hillsides. Native of south-eastern USA and the West Indies.

Seven Year Apple
Cassasia clusiifolia   Rubiaceae
Fleshy-leaved, semi-deciduous shrub growing up to 10 feet high. Rare and localized at one rocky coastal site in Castle Harbour.

Rhacoma
Crossopetalum rhacoma (syn. *Myginda crossopetalum*)
(syn. *Rhacoma crossopetalum*)   Celastraceae
Evergreen shrub growing up to 5 feet high. Rare and localized in an upland habitat in Southampton Parish only. Endangered.

Doc Bush
Baccharis glomeruliflora   Compositae
An evergreen shrub reaching a height of 10 feet. Widespread and uncommon in peat marshes, a good stand in the Devonshire Marsh. Uncommon and localized in upland habitats.

Wax Myrtle
Myrica cerifera   Myrtaceae
Evergreen shrub growing up to 20 feet high. Widespread and common in peat marshes. A good stand in Devonshire Marsh. Rare and localized in upland habitats.

And cactuses, a queen might don
If weary of a golden crown
And still appear as royal.

Elizabeth Browning

TASSEL PLANT
Suriana maritima

SPANISH
BAYONET
Yucca aloifolia

SEVEN YEAR
APPLE
*Cassasia
clusiifolia*

RHACOMA
Crossopetalumrhacoma

DOC BUSH
*Baccharis
glomeruliflora*

WAX MYRTLE
Myrica cerifera

6 Native coastal and salt-marsh plants

Spanish Bayonet

Yucca aloifolia   Agavaceae

A small tree with stiff rosettes of leaves growing from woody trunks. The sword-like leaves are to be respected. Flowers in tall clusters – cream in colour with purple markings. Commonly seen along the coastline.

Seaside Heliotrope

Heliotropum curassavicum   Boraginaceae

Found in salt-marsh and seashore habitats, the grey-green foliage has flowers on a slightly twirled stem. They are white with yellow and purple throats. Possibly came to Bermuda by floating seed.

Coast Sophora

Sophora tomentosa   Leguminosae

Leaves silver, grey-green, oblong-pinnate, flowers yellow with long seed pods. Sometimes seen on coastal rocks.

Beach Lobelia

Scaevola plumieri   Goodeniaceae

A dune colonizing shrub which grows up to 24 inches. Thick, fleshy leaves. Not commonly seen except along undisturbed coastal areas. Flowers unusual, white 5-lobed, irregular shape black fruits.

Sea Lavender (dark blue)

Limonium nashii   Plumbagnaceae

Found in salt-marsh clearings, flowering in early summer with a tiny line of purple-white flowers. Not often seen on the Bermudas.

Coast Spurge

Euphorbia buxifolia   Euphorbiaceae

Common on coastal rocks. A low-growing, fleshy plant with stiff stems, tiny ovate-oblong leaves, dull green with red markings. Free from hairs.

Bay Bean

Canavali lineata   Leguminosae

Found growing along the south shore beaches. Leather-like lobed leaves, pale purple flowers. Large seed pods with good crops of rounded beans. A good plant to grow in your garden. Likes sandy soil.

Beach Croton

Croton punctatus   Euphorbiaceae

A very hardy shrub found growing on sandy soils close to the coastline. Slightly grey leaves with ginger tone and speckled markings on the backside of the leaves. A good stand can be seen at Horseshoe Bay.

Sea Ox-Eye

Borrichia arborescens   Compositae

Found in both grey and green forms. Succulent in texture. Flowers yellow, attractive seed head that crumbles with winter winds.

Scurvy Grass

Cakile lanceolata   Cruciferae

One of the most characteristic dune plants. The succulent leaves can be used in salad, adding a spicy taste. Flowers are typically four-petalled and white.

Seaside Morning Glory

Ipomoea pes-caprae   Convolvulaceae

Found growing along many of the world's tropical beaches. The large pink flowers appear in the summer, the glossy-lobed leaves grow rampantly as the plant creeps along the sand dunes.

Wild Stock

Matthiola incana   Cruciferae

Found in coastal areas. The south shore roadside has a good stand. Leaves grey-green oblong, flowers purple, seed pod long and narrow.

Sea Purslane

Sesuvium portulacastrum   Portulacaceae

Seen frequently in salt-marsh habitats. Very fleshy, branching stems, prostrate growth forming dense patches. Flowers pale pink from the axils of leaf.

Iodine Bush (Sea Lavender)

Mallotonia gnaphalodes   Boraginaceae

Frequently seen along coastal beaches, among the rocks. Grey-green, silky leaves, very branched, in large clumps. Cream-white flowers with deep red markings, fruit black.

Seaside Evening Primrose

Oenothera humifusa   Onagraceae

Flowers yellow, turning to orange as the day evolves. Flowers summer to autumn. Foliage silvery-pubescent appearance. Found along sand dune habitats.

Seaside Goldenrod

Solidago sempervirens   Compositae

Leaves growing in 2-5 pairs on the stem, oblong lanceolate. Showy bracts and bright yellow flowers. Seed very plentiful, windblown. Fairly commonly seen.

These lovely birds, pure and fair
May serve as messengers to bear
My dear to one as fair as they
Who fills my thoughts from day
to day-

SPANISH BAYONET
Yucca aloifolia

SEASIDE HELIOTROPE
Heliotropum curassavicum

COAST SOPHORA
Sophora tomentosa

BEACH LOBELIA
Scaevola plumieri

BAY BEAN
Canavali lineata

SEA OX-EYE
Borrichia arborescens

grey form.

SEA LAVENDER
Limonium nashii

COAST PURGE
Euphorbia buxifolia

BEACH CROTON
Croton punctatus

WILD STOCK
Matthiola incana

SCURVY GRASS
Cakile lanceolata

SEASIDE MORNING GLORY
Ipomoea pes-caprae

SEA PURSLANE
Sesuvium portulacastrum

IODINE BUSH
Mallotonia gnaphalodes

SEASIDE EVENING PRIMROSE
Oenothera humifusa

SEASIDE GOLDENROD
Solidago sempervirens

Glandular Eupatorium

Eupatorium adenophorum　　　　Compositae
Found in very few areas, flowering in the springtime. Native of Mexico.

Indian Mallow

Abutilon theophrasti　　　　Malvaceae
Native to southern Asia. A naturalized weed in the USA. Commonly seen along cultivated fields, a very attractive plant but considered to be a weed. Flowers yellow, in the late summer.

Elderberry

Sambucus nigra　　　　Caprifoliaceae
From Europe, Africa and Asia. Tiny cream flowers. A large stand of Sambucus grows on the edge of Paget Marsh, and occasional roadsides. Berries black, edible. A popular drink today is Elderflower made by boiling the flowers in water, adding sugar and a touch of vinegar.

Heath Fire Cracker

Russelia equisetiformis　　　　Scrophulariaceae
Naturalized from the West Indies. A much branched shrub with bright red, tubular flowers. A garden escape that now covers hillsides and hedgerows. Still planted in gardens as ground cover.

Knotted Spike Rush

Eleocharis interstincta　　　　Cyperaceae
Found in marshland habitats including Devonshire Marsh. Native to eastern USA, the West Indies and tropical continental America.

Marsh Eclipta

Verbena alba　　　　Verbenaceae
Native to south-east USA and tropical America. Quite common in marshland habitats.

Small White Eupatorium

Eupatorium riparium　　　　Compositae
Many small genera of Compositae 1200 sp. This species is thought to have escaped from cultivation. Native of South America. Naturalized in the mountains of Jamaica. Flowers winter-spring.

Sea Rush

Juncus maritimus　　　　Juncaceae
Native to Europe and the coast of eastern USA. Not commonly seen but found occasionally in salt-marsh habitats, notably at the east end of Spittal Pond.

Poison Ivy

Rhus radicans　　　　Anacardiaceae
Clinging roots, severe dermatitis caused from its poison, blister-like growths appear in its peak season, but the winter stems are equally as dangerous. Found occasionally in hedgerows, marshes, etc. Once it has a hold it can take over a whole woodland, enveloping other plants in its way.

Burr Bush

Triumfetta semitriloba　　　　Tiliaceae
Native to Florida, West Indies and continental tropical America. Found in wild habitats, sometimes on waste ground. Flowers late summer.

Salt Marsh Ox-Eye

Borrichia frutescens　　　　Compositae
Native to USA. Thought to have reached Bermuda by floating. Found along salt-marsh and lagoon habitats. A large stand under the Mangroves at Walsingham. Yellow flowers and grey foliage bring light to the dark areas of the Mangrove roots.

Marsh Pennywort

Hydrocotyle umbellatus　　　　Umbelliferae
Native to east USA and England and the West Indies. Found in shady, moist areas; creeping stem.

Beard Grass

Andropogon glomeratus　　　　Graminae
From tropical America. Has recently become naturalized, notably along hillsides above Ferry Reach. Conspicuous in late summer when its flower heads turn golden brown.

Purslane

Portulaca oleracea　　　　Portulacaceae
Common in salt-marshes and along coastal rocks and sand, but a native weed of arable land. Yellow flowers are almost missed amidst the fleshy stems and leaves. Seen from spring to autumn.

Ruellia, Mexican

Ruellia brittoniana　　　　Acanthacea
A slender, upright, herbaceous perennial. Introduced this century as an ornamental garden plant that has become naturalized in a number of localities. Blue-purple tubular flowers, seen late summertime.

And down on knees
Anon – right I me set,
And as I could
This freshe flower I greet
Kneeling alway
Till it unclosed was
Upon the smalle
Softe sweete grass.

Chaucer

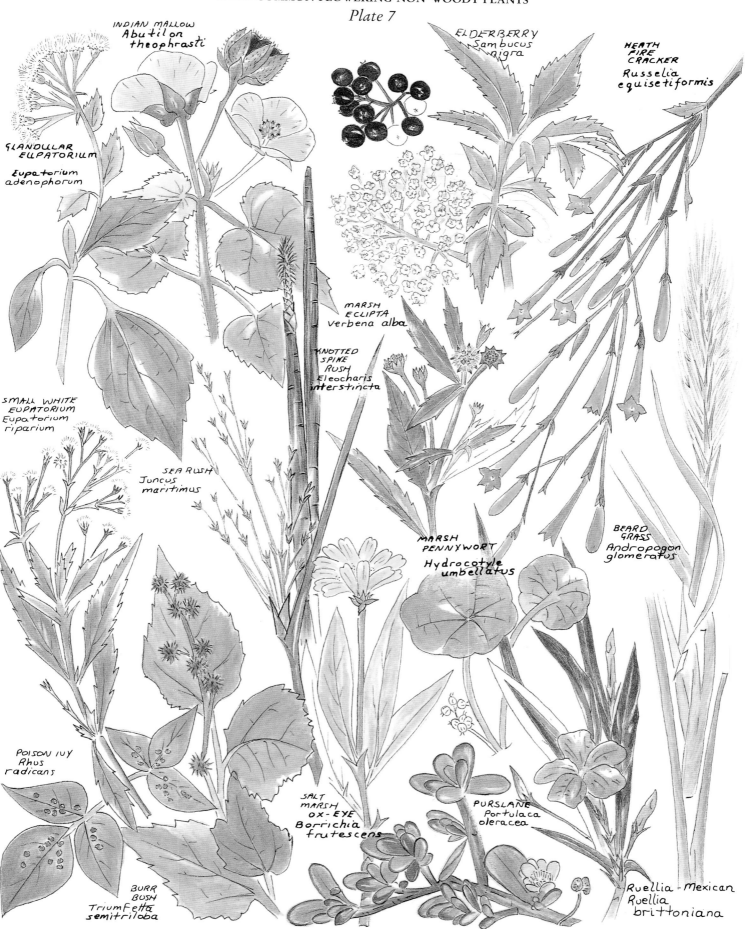

INDIAN MALLOW
Abutilon
theophrasti

GLANDULAR
EUPATORIUM
Eupatorium
adenophorum

ELDERBERRY
Sambucus
nigra

HEATH
FIRE
CRACKER
Russelia
equisetiformis

MARSH
ECLIPTA
Verbena alba

KNOTTED
SPIKE
RUSH
Eleocharis
interstincta

SMALL WHITE
EUPATORIUM
Eupatorium
riparium

SEA RUSH
Juncus
maritimus

MARSH
PENNYWORT
Hydrocotyle
umbellatus

BEARD
GRASS
Andropogon
glomeratus

POISON IVY
Rhus
radicans

SALT
MARSH
OX-EYE
Borrichia
frutescens

PURSLANE
Portulaca
oleracea

BURR
BUSH
Triumfetta
semitriloba

Ruellia - Mexican
Ruellia
brittoniana

Milkweed

Asclepias curassavica — Asclepiadaceae
Common in pasture land and some wasteland. Native of tropical America. Stems slightly woody, faintly pubescent. Bright orange petals with yellow erect hoods. Seeds 3 inches long and slightly curved. A habitat feeding paradise for the Monarch butterfly.

Rouge Plant

Rivina humilis — Phytolacaceae
Seen throughout the island in undisturbed habitats. A low shrub with tiny white flowers and bright red berries (that are sometimes called bloodberrys, the red fruits house a strong red dye). Introduced from North America. Naturalized in Europe. Flowers throughout the summer.

Ladies Tresses Orchid

Spiranthes spiralis — Orchidaceae
Asia, Europe and New World. Roots fibrous-tuberous. Erect, hardy, sub-tropical perennial terrestrial orchids, suited to shaded locations in moist soil. Found in a marsh on the Islands. Leafy at the base, flowers small, forming spirally twisted racemes.

Terrestrial Orchid

Zeuxine strateumatica — Orchidaceae
Naturalized at a locality where a native orchid 'Spiranthes' was reported in Britton's flora. Localized in wet pasture, edge of Devonshire peat marsh. Endangered.

Beach Alternanthera

Achyranthes maritima — Amaranthaceae
Likes beach exposures – Somerset Long Bay has a good stand, quite prostrate. It can tumble over walls or anything in its path if allowed to run wild. Found in southern Florida, The Bahamas and South America.

St Andrew's Cross

Ascyrum macrosepalum — Cuttiferae
(syn. *Hypericum macrosepalum*)
Endemic. Rare in peat marsh savannahs where fire can occur. Extremely rare. Can be seen localized at some dry, scrubby upland sites. Endangered.

Beaked Spike Rush

Eleocharis rostellata — Cyperaceae
Found in a few of the local marshlands, native to the USA and Cuba. Slender stems that grow densely once their roots are established.

Stipitate Beaked Rush

Rynchospora stipitata — Cyperaceae
In wet pastures and fields on the edge of Devonshire Marsh. Frequently seen along marshlands. Flowers in summer-autumn. Native to Florida.

Wood Grass

Oplismenus hirtellus — Gramineae
Native. Rare and localized under forest canopy of Paget Marsh and Walsingham upland sites. Also seen on some Hamilton Harbour islands.

Marsh Samphire or Woody Glasswort

Salicornia europaea — Chenopodiaceae
A coastal salt-marsh plant, very succulent with scale-like, jointed nodes to 18 inches. Flowers are tiny, can be eaten like spinach but rarely used by locals of Bermuda. Found growing along undisturbed bays in great abundance. Occasionally seen in limestone rocky pockets bordering inland tidal pools.

Lesser Bullrush or Cattail (Narrow leaved)

Typha angustifolia — Gramineae
Native and widely found in tropical and temperate regions of the world. In Bermuda commonly found in marshes; seed came by wind from America or West Indies. Flowers in the spring, furry spikes mature in autumn. Seems to reach 8 feet high. Feather-like seeds, blown off by the wind.

Showy Tick Trefoil

Desmodium canadense — Leguminosae
Found growing on harbour side of Point Shares, up to 2 feet tall. Purple-rose flowers in dense racemes. Pods hairy and cling to one. An introduced pest of paths and lawns.

Widgeon Grass or Beaked Tasselweed

Ruppia maritima — Ruppiaceae
Found in brackish ponds and in dense thickets along pondsides. Whitish stems, fruits in clusters.

Ditchweed (Hornwort)

Ceratophyllum demersum — Ceratophyllceae
Native to the USA. Leaves often crowded by the shortening of the internodes. Stalks 2-8 feet long.

Mermaid Weed

Proserpinaca palustris — Haloragidaceae
Naturalized in Bermuda, occurs in North America, and the West Indies. Only occasionally found in quiet, unspoiled wild areas. This plant has been cultivated and used in aquaria.

Bermuda Sedge

Carex bermudiana — Cyperaceae
Endemic. Extremely rare and localized. Grows well under native canopy in Paget Marsh. Also in two other upland sites in Warwick and Pembroke Parishes. Endangered.

Short Leaved Kyllinga

Kyllinga brevifolia — Cyperaceae
Commonly seen along marsh borders. Native of south-eastern USA, the West Indies and tropical America.

Water Fern

Salvinia rotundifolia — Salviniaceae
The floating fern, with its inflated leaves, is a naturalized species. It is not a true fern but related to ferns. Commonly found in ditches bordering the edge of marshes; often in a dense green mat.

The butterfly wanted to find himself a sweetheart. Of course, one of the nice little flowers was what he wanted. So he had a look at them. But what a lot there were to choose from!

Hans Christian Anderson

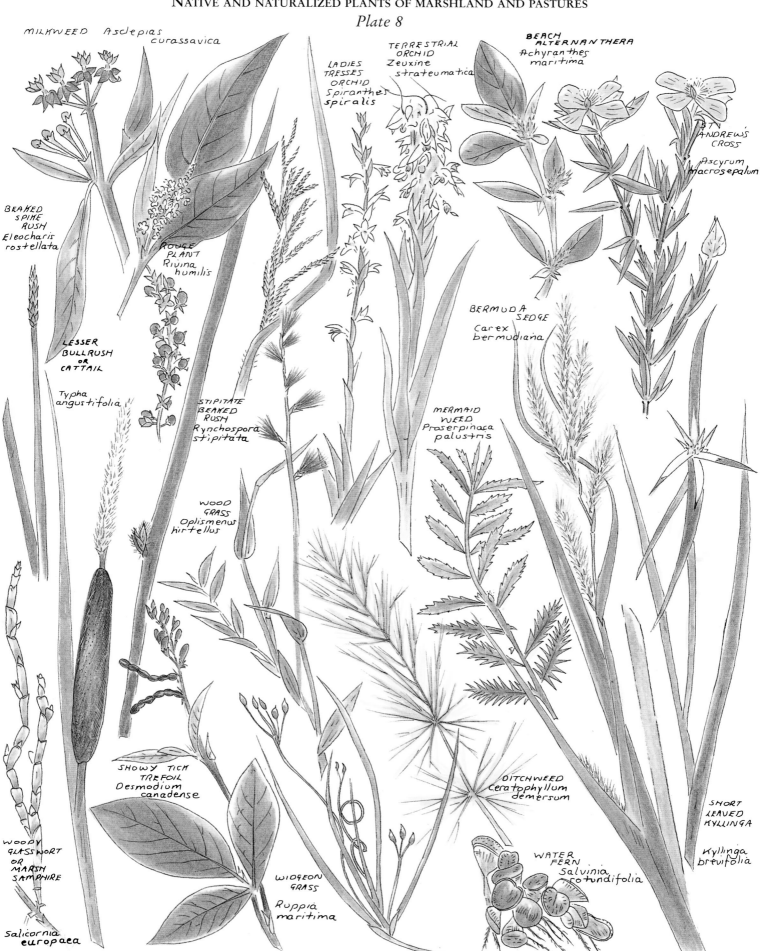

MILKWEED Asclepias curassavica

LADIES TRESSES ORCHID Spiranthes spiralis

TERRESTRIAL ORCHID Zeuxine strateumatica

BEACH ALTERNANTHERA Achyranthes maritima

BEAKED SPIKE RUSH Eleocharis rostellata

ST. ANDREW'S CROSS Ascyrum macrosepalum

ROUGE PLANT Rivina humilis

LESSER BULLRUSH OR CATTAIL Typha angustifolia

BERMUDA SEDGE Carex bermudiana

STIPITATE BEAKED RUSH Rynchospora stipitata

MERMAID WEED Proserpinaca palustris

WOOD GRASS Oplismenus hirtellus

SHOWY TICK TREFOIL Desmodium canadense

DITCHWEED Ceratophyllum demersum

SHORT LEAVED KYLLINGA Kyllinga brevifolia

WOODY GLASSWORT OR MARSH SAMPHIRE

WIDGEON GRASS Ruppia maritima

WATER FERN Salvinia rotundifolia

Salicornia europaea

False Mallow
Malvastrum coromandelianum   Malvaceae
Seen frequently along waste and cultivated ground. Flowers from spring to autumn, very pale yellow-orange.

Cranesbill (Small flowered)
Geranium pusillum   Geraniaceae
Found along arable and waste ground, tiny pink flowers seen in the spring and summertime.

Wood Vetch
Vicia sylvatica   Leguminosae
Found occasionally along edges of woodland and farmland. Climbing tendrils, purple flowers.

Tufted Vetch
Vicia cracca   Leguminosae
Commonly seen along the banks alongside farmland.

South American Vervain
Verbena bonariensis   Verbenaceae
Naturalized in Bermuda, seen in field and wasteland habitats.

Henbit (Dead Nettle)
Lamium amplexicaule   Labiatae
Native of Europe and naturalized in Bermuda. Commonly seen on waste and cultivated land. Can be seen flowering for much of the year. Calyx quite hairy, colour purple.

Field Woundwort
Stachys arvensis   Labiatae
Naturalized native, flowering in the spring and lasting through the summer. Frequently seen on the wasteland and borders of fields, etc. Foliage has many hairs, pale purple flowers.

Jamaica Weed
Nama jamaicense   Hydrophyllaceae
Seen along waste and cultivated grounds. Foliage full of hairs, corolla white-pale purple.

False Nettle
Boehmeria cylindrica   Urticaceae
Seen in marsh and wasteland habitats. Flowers seen most of the year.

Gallant Soldier
Galinsoga parviflòra   Compositae
Found along cultivated ground, introduced to the Botanical Gardens in 1908.

Cockroach Poison
Solanum robustum   Solanaceae
Found in wasteland and undisturbed gardens. In the summer, tiny white flowers with yellow anthers are seen. Its broad leaves are tough with spiky margins.

Wood Cudweed
Gnaphalium sylvaticum   Compositae
Found in clearings and old-established gardens. Flower heads on a long, leafy spike.

Low Cudweed or Marsh Cudweed
Gnaphalium viliginosum   Compositae
Occasionally seen in sandy soil. Flowers in the springtime. Possibly reached Bermuda on the wind.

Thin Runner Willowherb
Epilobium obscurum   Onagraceae
Found along roadsides and wasteland. Tiny pink flowers in spring and early summer.

Bear's Foot
Polymnia uvedalia   Compositae
Originally from the eastern USA. Found on rocky/sandy hilly outcrops. Leaves broad and deltoid in shape, pubescent. Flowers in spring. Flowers bright yellow, seeds form in a cup shape.

Long Leaved Dock
Rumex longifolius   Polygonaceae
Quite commonly seen along most open space habitats. Flowers in the spring.

Apple of Peru or Shoo Fly Plant
Nicandra physaloides   Solanaceae
Seen occasionally along farmland/wasteland habitats. Naturalized, flowers all throughout the summer, pale purple.

Just living is not enough
said the butterfly –
One must have sunshine,
freedom and little flowers.

Hans Christian Anderson.

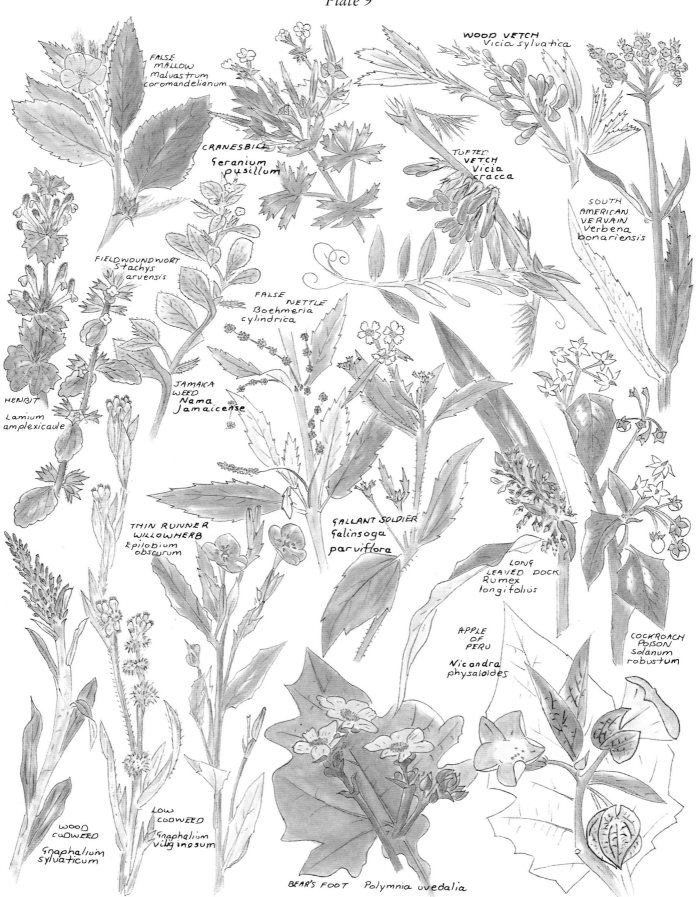

FALSE MALLOW Malvastrum coromandelianum

CRANESBILL Geranium pusillum

WOOD VETCH Vicia sylvatica

TUFTED VETCH Vicia cracca

SOUTH AMERICAN VERVAIN Verbena bonariensis

FIELD WOUNDWORT Stachys arvensis

FALSE NETTLE Boehmeria cylindrica

HENBIT Lamium amplexicaule

JAMAICA WEED Nama Jamaicense

THIN RUNNER WILLOWHERB Epilobium obscurum

GALLANT SOLDIER Galinsoga parviflora

LONG LEAVED DOCK Rumex longifolius

APPLE OF PERU Nicandra physaloides

COCKROACH POISON Solanum robustum

WOOD CUDWEED Gnaphalium sylvaticum

LOW CUDWEED Gnaphalium uliginosum

BEAR'S FOOT Polymnia uvedalia

Coliseum Ivy

Cymbalaria muralis   Scrophulariaceae

Native of Europe. A very dainty plant found trailing over hedgerows and walls. Rooting at the nodes. Lilac colour flowers.

Poinsettia (Joseph's Coat) (or Japanese Poinsettia)

Euphorbia heterophylla   Euphorbiaceae

Second largest angiosperm genus. Shrubs and trees with milky latex-stems, often spiny. Found locally in many habitats, likes rocky banks. Flowers throughout the year.

Prickly Poppy

Agrimone mexicana   Papaveraceae

Naturalized from tropical America. Leaves spiny-toothed, bright yellow flowers, orange sap. Seen on waste and cultivated land.

Creeping Day Flower

Commelina longicaulis   Commelinaceae

Naturalized. Tiny blue flowers. Found in undisturbed open spaces and cultivated land.

Poinsettia, Annual

Poinsettia cyathophora   Euphorbiaceae

Commonly seen, particularly on cultivated ground and rocky banks. The bright red bracts stand out along most roadside hedgerows. A milky latex that is common in Euphorbias.

Stinging Nettle (Labiate)

Urtica dioica   Urticaceae

A commonly seen plant in Bermuda with a very cosmopolitan distribution range. It is found in most northern temperatures. Has stinging hairs, flowers hang in catkin-like form at each node on the female plants. Was used for cloth up until the eighteenth century, and is still used today in parts of Asia as a palatable soup.

Jamaica Vervain

Valerianodes jamaicensis   Verbenaceae

Tiny lilac flowers on long blades. Growing along hedgerows, often next to cultivated land and open spaces.

Wall Speedwell

Veronica arvensis   Scrophulariaceae

Seen in waste and cultivated ground. Naturalized native of Europe. Tiny blue flowers.

Balloon Vine

Cardiospermum halicacabum   Sapindaceae

Found growing in hedgerows and gardens where given the space to climb. The tendrils cling onto other vegetation. Small white-yellow flowers, fruits black on thin-shelled, inflated capsules.

White Beggars' Ticks

Bidens pilosa   Compositae

Found growing along most roadsides, waste and cultivated land. Naturalized. The white flowers are a common sight along Bermuda's roads.

Opium (Garden Poppy)

Papaver somniferum   Papaveraceae

Lilac-purple flowers. Found mostly in fields unploughed in early summer. From the Mediterranean or the Middle East. Poppy seeds are used for baking breads, cakes, etc.

Prostrate Spurge

Chamaesyce prostrata   Euphorbiaceae

Very much like coastal spurge in habit. Branched from the base, leaves green-deep red. Flowers throughout the year with off-white petals.

Rhombic-leaved Sida

Sida rhombifolia   Malvaceae

Native of the southern USA and tropical America. Flowers from spring to autumn. Pale yellow flowers, leaves and seed always appear brittle. Found in open spaces close to cultivated land.

Wire Weed

Sida carpinifolia   Malvaceae

Commonly seen, dwarf, hibiscus-like flowers of dull orange-grey-green, leaves with crenate margins. Would make a nice ground cover. From the Pacific islands.

Smooth-Fruited Poppy

Papaver dubium   Papaveraceae

Likes sandy soil. Flowers bright red, late April/early May. Found in arable and wasteland habitats. Foliage covered in hairs. The lilac Opium Poppy and the red Corn Poppy can also be seen but not as commonly.

God make my life a little light,
Within the world to glow.
A little flame that burneth bright
Wherever I may go.
God make my life a little flower,
That giveth joy to all,
Content to bloom in native bower
although the place be small.
God make my life a little song,
that comforteth the sad,
That helpeth others to be strong,
and makes the singer glad.

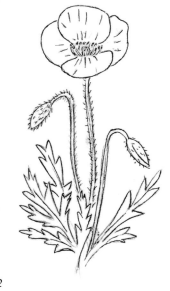

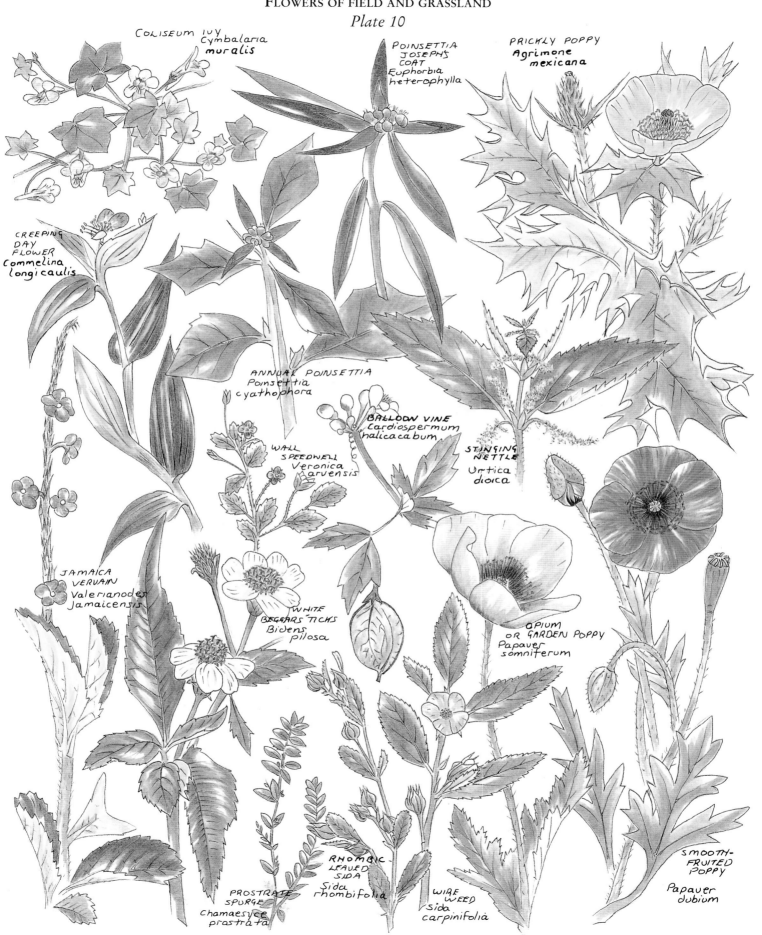

COLISEUM IVY
Cymbalaria
muralis

POINSETTIA
JOSEPHS
COAT
Euphorbia
heterophylla

PRICKLY POPPY
Agrimone
mexicana

CREEPING
DAY
FLOWER
Commelina
longicaulis

ANNUAL POINSETTIA
Poinsettia
cyathophora

BALLOON VINE
Cardiospermum
halicacabum

WALL
SPEEDWELL
Veronica
arvensis

STINGING
NETTLE

Urtica
dioica

JAMAICA
VERVAIN
Valerianodes
jamaicensis

WHITE
BEGGARS TICKS
Bidens
pilosa

OPIUM
OR GARDEN POPPY
Papaver
somniferum

PROSTRATE
SPURGE

Chamaesyce
prostrata

RHOMBIC-
LEAVED
SIDA
Sida
rhombifolia

WIRE
WEED
Sida
carpinifolia

SMOOTH-
FRUITED
POPPY

Papaver
dubium

11 Field and wayside plants

White Daisy
Chrysanthemum leucanthemum   Compositae
Naturalized. Seen mostly on grassland, growing up to 12
inches high.

Spiny Sow Thistle
Sonchus asper   Compositae
Leaves clasping, stem ribbed, seed seen on waste and farmland.

Daisy Fleabane
Erigeron annus   Compositae
Found in undisturbed grasslands. Naturalized. Tiny daisy-like
flowers are pale purple. Established plants branch, leaves
slightly hairy, stems erect.

Blue Pimpernel
Anagallis arvensis var. caerulea   Primulaceae
Flowers blue or scarlet. Found occasionally in grassland,
attractive and low growing.

Scarlet Pimpernel
Anagallis arvensis   Primulaceae
Flowers found occasionally in grassland and borders of arable
fields.

Pink Centurium
Centaurium pulchellum   Gentianaceae
A native of England. The tiny pink flowers appear in grass and
wasteland.

Common Chickweed
Stellaria media   Caryophyllaceae
Seen frequently on waste and cultivated land. From Europe,
naturalized in North America. Flowers white, spring to
summer.

Sow Thistle
Sonchus oleraceus   Compositae
Found growing wild on cultivated land, treated as a weed. A
good fodder plant.

Fine-leaved Sandwort
Minuartia hybrida   Caryophyllaceae
A native English plant that likes sandy soils. Seen flowering in
June.

Wild Pepper Grass
Lepidium campestre   Cruciferae
Small white flowers, tiny seed pods, leaves toothed. A fairly
common weed in fields and open spaces.

Stiff Verbena
Verbena rigida   Verbenaceae
Erect growth, leaves 2-3 inches long, oblong, stiff and roughly
hairy. Seen often along farmland hedgerows.

Yellow Melilot
Melilotus indica   Leguminosae
Naturalized from Europe. Found growing in waste and
cultivated habitats. Stems erect with branched leaflets, yellow
flowers and tiny oval seed pods.

Black Medic
Medicago lupulina   Leguminosae
Looking like a tiny yellow clover, this plant creeps through the
grass lawns. Tiny seed pods.

Fumitory
Fumaria muralis   Fumariaceae
Common on waste ground and farmland. Tiny, pink-purple
flowers seen for much of the year along farmland and other
open spaces.

Large Mouse-Ear Chickweed
Cerastium vulgatum   Caryophyllaceae
Seen in fields and wasteland. A native of Europe.

Mouse-Ear Chickweek
Cerastium cerastoides   Caryophyllaceae
Naturalized. Originally from Europe. Seen on waste and
grassland. The flowers and foliage of the chickweeds are so
similar they are difficult to identify one from another.

Baldwin's Chickweed
Stellaria baldwinii   Caryophyllaceae
Found growing in grassland and fields, locally seen as a weed.

Mustard
Brassica nigra   Cruciferae
A common weed, especially in fields. Commonly seen also in
Europe and America. Three other species grow on the Islands.
They all look very similar with cream-yellow, white-pink
flowers. Elongated seeds.

Toothed Medic
Medicago polymorpha   Leguminosae
Naturalized from Europe. Found commonly in fields,
wasteland and lawns. The spiral twisted seed is a problem for
pets and clothes as it clings like a claw.

Spiny Fruited Crowfoot
Ranunculus muricatus   Ranunculaceae
Ranunculus species occur globally and are known as
buttercups because of their yellow flowers. Generally found in
wild areas, fields and grasslands.

Narrow-Leaved Vetch
Vicia angustifolia   Leguminosae
Found alongside cultivated land. Naturalized. Flowers spring-
summer, purple.

Hedge Mustard
Erysimum officinale   Cruciferae
Flowers pale yellow. Found in undisturbed farmland.
Naturalized.

Flower in the crannied wall
I hold you here, root and all
in my hand
Little flower but if I could
understand what you are,
Root and all, and all in all
I should know what God
and man is.

Alfred, Lord Tennyson

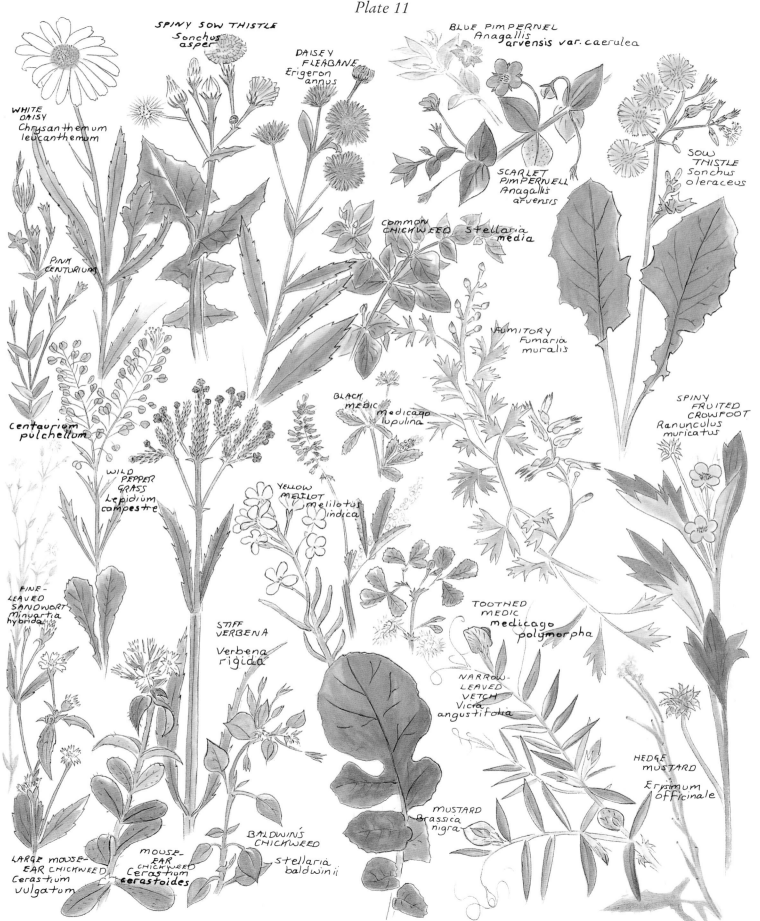

SPINY SOW THISTLE
Sonchus asper

DAISEY FLEABANE
Erigeron annus

BLUE PIMPERNEL
Anagallis arvensis var. caerulea

WHITE DAISY
Chrysanthemum leucanthemum

SCARLET PIMPERNELL
Anagallis arvensis

SOW THISTLE
Sonchus oleraceus

PINK CENTAURIUM

COMMON CHICKWEED Stellaria media

FUMITORY
Fumaria muralis

Centaurium pulchellum

BLACK MEDIC medicago lupulina

SPINY FRUITED CROWFOOT
Ranunculus muricatus

WILD PEPPER GRASS
Lepidium campestre

YELLOW MELLOT melilotus indica

FINE-LEAVED SANDWORT
Minuartia hybrida

STIFF VERBENA
Verbena rigida

TOOTHED MEDIC
medicago polymorpha

NARROW-LEAVED VETCH
Vicia angustifolia

HEDGE MUSTARD
Erysimum officinale

BALDWIN'S CHICKWEED
Stellaria baldwinii

MUSTARD
Brassica nigra

LARGE MOUSE-EAR CHICKWEED
Cerastium vulgatum

MOUSE-EAR CHICKWEED
Cerastium cerastoides

Marvel of Peru
Mirabilis jalapa — Nyctaginaceae
A group of interesting, often fragile perennial herbs from tropical America. In the wild, giant tubers may weigh up to 44 pounds (rarely seen in cultivation). Flowers are long, tubular, fragrant and vary in colour from white to crimson red. Occasionally yellow forms are seen. More commonly found in older garden situations but not widespread.

Small-Fruited Balloon Vine
Cardiospermum microcarpum — Sapindaceae
Native to Bermuda. Common in reserves and native areas. Climbing often on ground space. Finely pubescent, slender, grooved stem. Leaves thin, small, white flowers. Capsule three-lobed revealing black seed attached, balloon-like capsule. Native to Florida, the West Indies and continental America.

Sweet Violet
Viola odorata — Violaceae
Found in flower gardens, originally from Europe. The purple flowers are quite fragrant.

Tobacco
Nicotiana tabacum — Solanaceae
Seen occasionally along hedgerows and sometimes grown as an ornamental border plant in flower gardens. A branching shrub with a pale yellow corolla, tube-shaped flower.

Hairy Spurge
Chamaesyce hirta — Euphorbiaceae
Frequently seen along cultivated ground. Naturalized, native to the West Indies and tropical America. Slender branched stems.

Pigweed
Chenopodium album — Chenopodiaceae
Thought of as a weed. Naturalized from Europe. Seen in wasteland and undisturbed areas.

Hypericum-leaved Spurge
Chamaesyce hypericifolia — Euphorbiaceae
Seen along waste and cultivated areas. Naturalized. Densely flowered.

Bird Pepper
Capsicum baccatum — Solanaceae
Grows up to 3 feet, produces bright red peppers which are often used for culinary purposes.

Hairy Horse-Weed
Leptilon linifoliun — Carduaceae
Common along waste and cultivated ground. Naturalized. Densely hairy foliage.

Horse-Weed Fleabane
Leptilon canadense — Carduaceae
Common as its sister plant above, but much taller. Seen as a weed.

Buttonweed
Borreria laevis — Rubiaceae
Native of the West Indies. Slightly hairy, flowers tiny white, in any month of the year. Seeds tiny, ovoid. Foliage deep green, leaves oblong to elliptical, lanceolate.

New Zealand Spinach
Tetragonia tetragonioides — Aizoaceae
Escaped from cultivation and has become naturalized. Can be found in most arable and salt-marsh areas. Stems prostrate and ascend to 18 feet. Solitary yellow flowers in leaf axil. Delicious in salad. Native of New Zealand.

Parthenium
Parthenium hysterophorus — Compositae
Naturalized. Common along waste and cultivated land. Tiny white flowers, with a mature plant growing up to 2 feet high.

Black Nightshade
Solanum nigrum — Solanaceae
Found in fallow derelict gardens and fields. A native plant which flowers periodically from spring to autumn. Seed possibly came to Bermuda by bird. Solanum species must be treated with extreme care as most contain poisonous chemicals which can be harmful if eaten.

Buds of yellow hue
Do paint the meadows
With delight.

Shakespeare

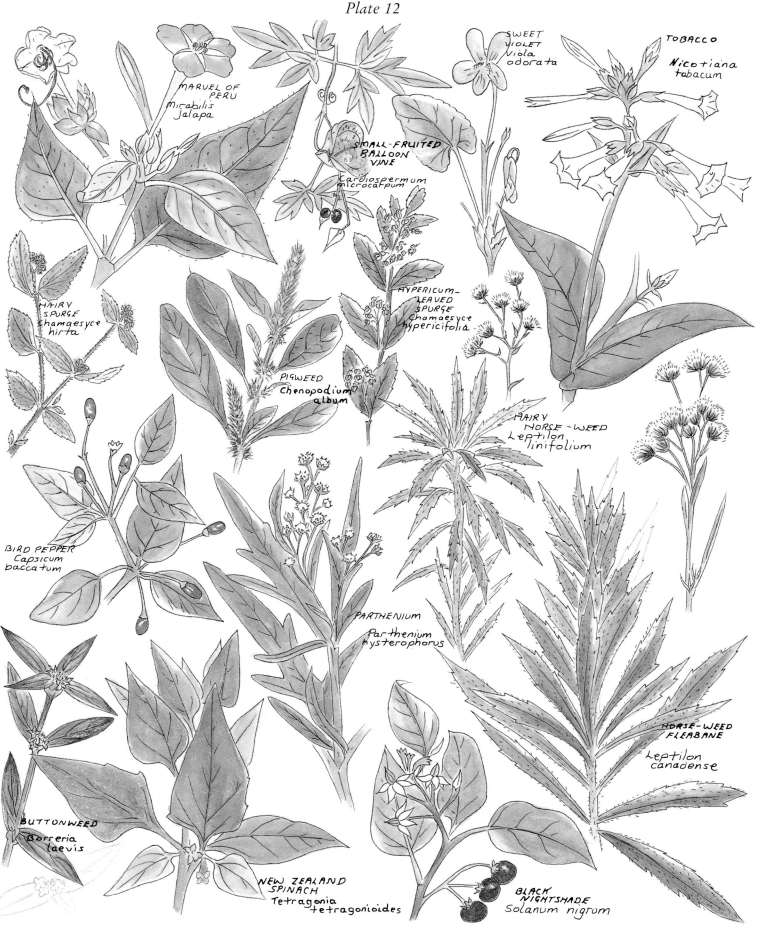

MARVEL OF PERU
Mirabilis jalapa

SMALL-FRUITED BALLOON VINE
Cardiospermum microcarpum

SWEET VIOLET
Viola odorata

TOBACCO
Nicotiana tabacum

HAIRY SPURGE
Chamaesyce hirta

HYPERICUM-LEAVED SPURGE
Chamaesyce hypericifolia

PIGWEED
Chenopodium album

HAIRY HORSE-WEED
Leptilon linifolium

BIRD PEPPER
Capsicum baccatum

PARTHENIUM
Parthenium hysterophorus

HORSE-WEED FLEABANE
Leptilon canadense

BUTTONWEED
Borreria laevis

NEW ZEALAND SPINACH
Tetragonia tetragonioides

BLACK NIGHTSHADE
Solanum nigrum

Castor Oil Plant

Ricinus communis   Euphorbiaceae

Known to have very poisonous seed yet an attractive plant. Its leaves have a bronze tint with many tones of dull green. When seeds ripen one can hear them pop. Found growing in many open spaces on uncultivated land. Flowers tiny and white.

Spanish Moss

Tillandsia usneoides   Bromeliaceae

South-east USA, Argentina and Chile. Growing from trees in masses of feathery silvery-grey threads, holding moisture from the air. Tiny flowers, yellowish-blue.

Mother-in-Law's Tongue

Sansevieria trifasciata   Agavaceae

Very erect plant with stiff leaves that grow very well in Bermuda. Quite succulent and leathery with variegated marking of deep green to grey, silver-yellow markings. Found growing wild and in cultivation. Flowers are greenish-white. From Eastern Province, Zaire.

Virgate Mimosa

Leucaena virgatum   Leguminosae

Native, not common. Noted in hedgerows in Somerset in Castle Harbour. Flowers in the spring throughout the summer. Thought to have been transported to Bermuda by bird. The thin narrow leaves are a miniature version of the Wild Mimosa.

Rice Paper Plant

Tetrapanax papyriferus   Araliaceae

Found growing mostly in old-established gardens. An attractive plant growing up to 8 feet high, sending up whirls of flower spikes.

Wild Mimosa or Jumbie Bean

Leucaena leucocephala   Leguminosae

From tropical America (naturalized elsewhere). Small shrub/tree with brown stems. Leaves two pinnate, leaflets 10-20 pairs, glaucous beneath. Flowers lemon-yellow in globose, fluffly heads, stamens five times as large as the petals.

Cestrum

Cestrum nocturnum   Solanaceae

From the West Indies. Occasionally planted as an ornamental shrub. Pale cream flowers. Grows to 8 feet. Seen along Vesey Street, Devonshire Marsh area.

Elephant's Ear

Philodendron giganteum   Araceae

Tropical America. Large epiphytic plant with entire perforated or pinnatifed leaves. Corky aerial roots. Holes in leaves caused by slowing of growth of lamina, drying and splitting as the rest expands. Common as house plants around the world.

Mexican or Brazilian Pepper Tree

Schinus terebinthifolius   Anacardiaceae

Originally from Brazil and Paraguay, sometimes known as the Mexican Pepper Tree or the Christmas Berry Tree. Its bright red berries are used for decoration at Christmas time. Tiny white-green flowers, seeded by wind and birds. Taking a strong hold in secondary forests.

Some herbs have grace.
Great weeds do grow apace.

Shakespeare

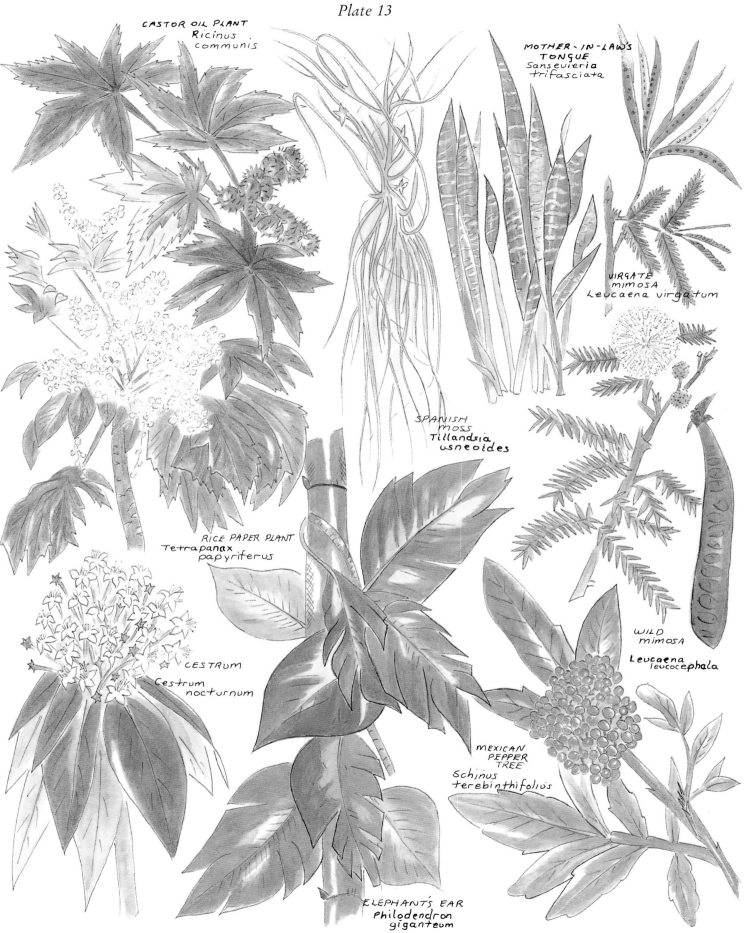

CASTOR OIL PLANT
Ricinus communis

MOTHER-IN-LAW'S TONGUE
Sansevieria trifasciata

VIRGATE MIMOSA
Leucaena virgatum

SPANISH MOSS
Tillandsia usneoides

RICE PAPER PLANT
Tetrapanax papyriferus

WILD MIMOSA
Leucaena leucocephala

CESTRUM
Cestrum nocturnum

MEXICAN PEPPER TREE
Schinus terebinthifolius

ELEPHANT'S EAR
Philodendron giganteum

Yellow Wood Sorrel (Bermuda Buttercup)
Oxalis pes-caprae   Oxalidaceae
Found growing in most grass borders in gardens of Bermuda.
The bright yellow flowers last into early summer and start
blooming in early spring. Native of South Africa.

Purple Wood Sorrel
Oxalis martiana   Oxalidaceae
Abundant weed in fields and grassland. Native, flowers from
autumn to spring.

Cape Weed
Lippia nodiflora   Verbenaceae
One of the most commonly seen native plants, abundant
islandwide. Seems to prefer dry areas. Originally from the old
world tropics. Possibly arrived in Bermuda with the wind or
birds. Leaves are strong and thick, the foliage creeps. The
flower heads reveal a mass of pale purple-white flowers.

Freesia
Freesia refracta-alba   Iridaceae
Seen commonly in fields and gardens. If allowed to set seed
large areas of grassland can be a total carpet of this lovely
scented flower. Leaves up to 12 inches long, flowers up to 3
inches long with delicate touches of yellow and purple on
creamy-white petals. Native of South Africa.

Wood Sorrel
Oxalis corniculata   Oxalidaceae
Commonly seen in waste and cultivated ground (thought of as
a weed). The flowers are very attractive and yellow.
Introduced. A native of tropical America, and the S. African
Cape. Flowers for much of the year.

Pink Bermudiana (Star of the Veldt)
Lapeirousia cruenta   Iridaceae
A delicate flower, with flat narrow leaves, flowers on a wiry
raceme. Long tubes with red petal lobes, deep orange-red with
deep red markings on three petals. Flowers in spring, March-
April. Can be found in carpets in established grass lawns.

Flopper or Life Plant
Bryophyllum pinnatum   Crassulaceae
Life plant, stout, 1-6 feet tall. Glabrous and more or less
glaucous. Leaves opposite, pinnate fleshy/leathery. Calyx
paper-like and much inflated, $1\frac{1}{2}$ inches long, green-yellow-
white tinted purple. Uncertain origins but now established and
growing wild everywhere.

Narcissus (Jonquil) (bunch flowered)
Narcissus tazetta   Amaryllidaceae
Originally from southern Europe and central Asia. Having
escaped from cultivation has now become naturalized in much
open space, gardens, hillsides, etc. Bulbous with narrow leaves.
Flowers on a nodding umbel, cream-white with pale yellow
markings on its small tubular flower. Seeds black.

Nasturtium
Tropaeolum majus   Tropaeolaceae
Native of Peru but commonly seen in many areas of the world.
In Bermuda it loves creeping and climbing in cultivated and
garden areas and hedgerows, also wasteland. Finely succulent
and glabrous, the almost round leaves are good in salad.
Flowers yellow-orange varieties, fruit 3-lobed. The flowers are
also edible. Bermudian locals often put them with salad or
sandwiches.

If I should plant a tiny seed
of love
in the garden of your heart
Would it grow to be a great big
love some day
Or would it die and fade away?
Would you care for it and tend it
every day
Till the time when all must part?
If I should plant a tiny seed
of love
in the garden of your heart.

A. Macdonald.
(J. Tate Feldman Co.)

YELLOW
WOOD
SORREL

BERMUDA
BUTTERCUP
Oxalis
pes-caprae

PURPLE WOOD
SORREL

Oxalis
martiana

CAPE WEED
Lippia nodiflora

FREESIA
Freesia
refracta
alba

WOOD SORREL
Oxalis
corniculata

PINK
BERMUDIANA

Lapeirousia
cruenta

NASTURTIUM
Tropaeolum
majus

NARCISSUS
OR JONQUIL

Narcissus
tazetta

FLOPPER
OR
LIFE PLANT

Bryophyllum
pinnatum

May Weed
Ammi majus — Umbelliferae
Found along south shore in hedgerows. An introduced plant scarcely seen. Up to 24 inches high, good for flower arranging. Flowers in May.

Fennel
Foeniculum vulgare — Umbelliferae
Originating from Europe and the Mediterranean region, it grows wild throughout the Bermuda Islands. It can reach up to 8 feet high. Occasionally used locally in salad and for garnish etc. Elsewhere it is cultivated commercially for essential oils and for food flavourings. Flower heads are a showy yellow, round flat umbrella like. Common along roadsides and waste ground areas. Enjoyed in local gardens; used for making soup, etc.

Red Justica
Justica secunda — Acanthaceae
Origins in tropics and sub-tropics. A shrub with 1-2 inch flowers, tubular red. Leaves ovate-oblong to lanceolate, up to 6 inches long, tapering to petiole-bracts smaller than calyx. Also found in North and South America. Used by Bermudians as a herbal remedy, locally known as 'Father John'.

Chicory
Chicorium intybus — Compositae
Native to Europe. Naturalized also in Bermuda and North America. Grows well in Bermuda where grass is not mown, occasionally seen in established hedgerows. It has a long taproot. Spatulate leaf outline with serrated edge. Sky-blue flowers. Can be used as a coffee substitute. An herbaceous perennial.

Prickly Pink Sage Bush
Lantana aculeata — Verbenaceae
A small shrub seen on hillsides and lanes where established flora have a hold. Native of tropical America, found flowering abundantly through summer and autumn. Flowers various yellow, orange and pink shades. Corolla stem tube shape, prickly with lanceolate leaves, quite hairy to touch.

Twiggy Mullein
Verbascum virgatum — Scrophulariaceae
A group of outstanding biennial herbs with large clusters of leaf rosettes, often grey in colour. May originate from the dry regions of the Mediterranean.

Dandelion
Taraxacum officinale — Compositae
Commonly seen in waste and cultivated habitats. Naturalized. A native plant of Europe. The root is thick and deep. Flowers yellow with attractive puffball seed heads. Children love to blow the seeds, musing that each blow is an hour and therefore they can guess the time.

Rosemary
Rosmarinus officinalis — Labiatae
Naturalized shrub sometimes seen in abundance on dry rocky hillsides. Flowers spring and summer. Planted not only for herbal uses but as a garden ornamental plant. Dense, tiny linear leaves on a woody stem. Flowers pale purple.

Wild Indigo
Indigofera suffruticosa — Leguminosae
Seen in jungle and protected habitats. Naturalized. Native to the West Indies. Said by Lefroy to have been introduced to Bermuda for commercial purposes in the seventeenth century. A lovely blue dye can be obtained from the leaves. Orange-scarlet flower, seed pods curved and in a mass.

Knotted Hedge Parsley
Torilis nodosa — Umbelliferae
Commonly seen in waste places, also cultivated ground and along hedgerows. Naturalized. A native of Europe, it is related to the Cow Parsley. Typical umbel-type flower head with prickly seed heads that seem to stick well to animals, and humans. Known also as Queen Anne's Lace.

Wild Sage Bush (Shrub Verbena)
Lantana camara — Verbenaceae
A small, branching shrub fairly prickly, rough and pubescent to the touch. Leaves mostly longish, ovate with finely serrated edge. Bright yellow-orange flowers with curved corolla in terminal clusters. Commonly seen on hillsides, fields and roadsides. Flowers from springtime through most of the year.

Alexanders
Smyrnium olusatrum — Umbelliferae
A member of the Parsley family which has become naturalized. Found growing mostly in established and some untouched hedgerows. Its root was once grated and used as a coconut substitute and other local and medicinal uses. Black, shiny seeds in umbels. Was used in the old days as a vegetable, like celery.

English Plantain
Plantago lanceolata — Plantaginaceae
Native of Europe, widely seen in the world today. Leaves lanceolate, long silvery hair often covers plant, expecially at base of stem. Flowers on spike with fat oval head, tiny lilac corolla. Found growing in grassland and mainly pasture and hedgerow environments.

Common Sage Bush
Lantana involucrata — Verbenaceae
The aptly named, most common of all the sage bushes in Bermuda, a small shrub whose fragrance has always been part of the Bermuda 'smell' (the air being full of the unforgettable flower scents). Leaves oval.

Common (Great) Plantain
Plantago major — Plantaginaceae
Native of Europe, now widely seen all over the world. Leaves abruptly contracted below to a petiol. Spike of flowers, green with lilac petals, forming a capsule with many seeds. Flowers all through the year.

Calamint
Clinopodium calamintha — Labiatae
Native of Europe. Quite common, especially on waste ground. Has naturalized in Bermuda. Flowers in summer and autumn. Leaves broadly ovate. Flowers with pale purple corolla, sometimes known as Catnip locally, but not the true Catnip.

Small White Sage
Salvia serotina — Labiatae
Commonly seen in hedgerows, rocky outcrops and waste ground where it has naturalized. Tiny lilac-white flowers are seen for much of the year. Branching stems grow up to 18 inches in height. These are slightly pubescent.

Scarlet Sage
Salvia coccinea — Labiatae
Quite a rare, attractive naturalized herb, once widespread now rapidly disappeaing due to roadside spraying. Native to south-west USA and Mexico. Flowers from spring to autumn. Corolla red, 0.5 inches in length, with elongated calyx and conspicuously ribbed, scented leaves.

Garden Parsley
Petroselinum crispum — Umbelliferae
Often seen thriving in coastal gardens. Both seeds and leaves are used for flavouring. Its distribution range includes vast areas of Europe.

There's Rosemary, that's for remembrance.

Hamlet
Shakespeare

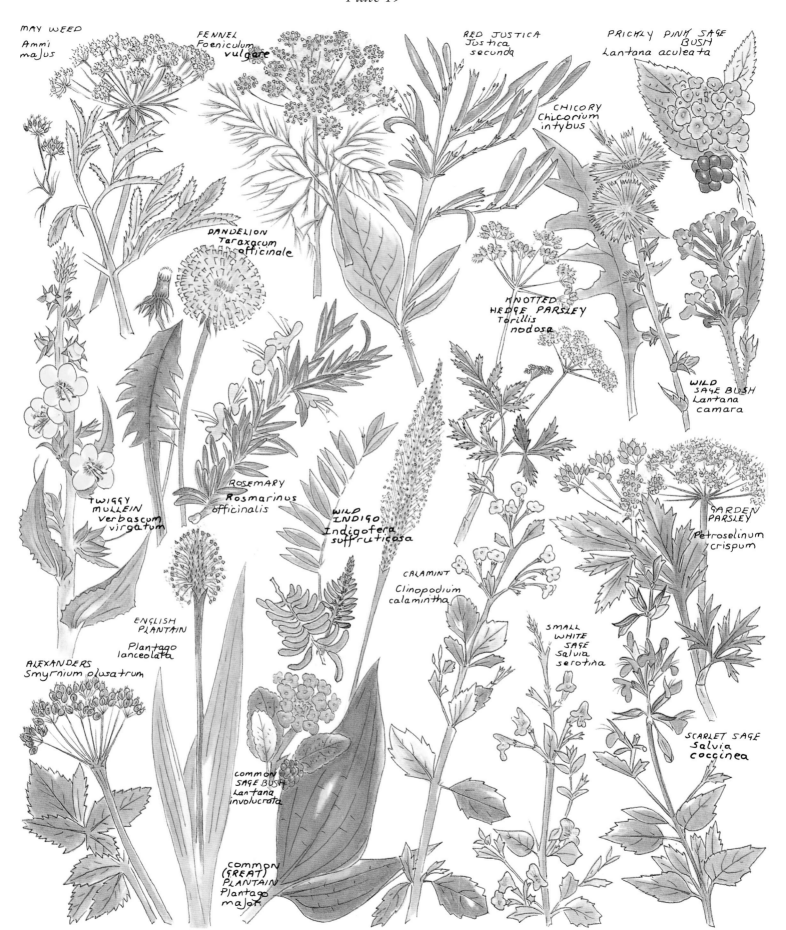

MAY WEED
Ammi majus

FENNEL
Foeniculum vulgare

RED JUSTICA
Justica secunda

PRICKLY PINK SAGE BUSH
Lantana aculeata

CHICORY
Chicorium intybus

DANDELION
Taraxacum officinale

KNOTTED HEDGE PARSLEY
Torillis nodosa

WILD SAGE BUSH
Lantana camara

TWIGGY MULLEIN
Verbascum virgatum

ROSEMARY
Rosmarinus officinalis

WILD INDIGO
Indigofera suffruticosa

GARDEN PARSLEY
Petroselinum crispum

CALAMINT
Clinopodium calamintha

SMALL WHITE SAGE
Salvia serotina

ENGLISH PLANTAIN
Plantago lanceolata

ALEXANDERS
Smyrnium olusatrum

COMMON SAGE BUSH
Lantana involucrata

SCARLET SAGE
Salvia coccinea

COMMON (GREAT) PLANTAIN
Plantago major

Morning Glory or Blue Dawn Flower

Ipomoea indica   Convolvulaceae

The most common in Bermuda of the vines that are known to be strong growing and often pest plants to the gardener. Although a beautiful plant to look at, it grows so prolifically, covering waste or unkept areas at up to one foot a day in the growing season. Its bright purple flowers do look wonderful when allowed to grow wild on sides of fields or marshes, often like purple cascading waterfalls.

Cut-Leaved Morning Glory

Ipomoea dissecta   Convolvulaceae

Sometimes called the Noya Vine, turning stems hirsute, 5-7 branching leaves, flowers white with purple throat. Found occasionally on waste ground and along roadsides – not commonly seen. Native of southern USA and the West Indies. Flowers summer and autumn.

Sweet Potato

Ipomoea batatas   Convolvulaceae

Seen often in undisturbed areas, introduced. Pale purple flowers, rootstock edible but only eaten from cultivated plants. (Wild species sketched.)

White Morning Glory

Turbinia corymbosa   Convolvulaceae

Seen growing wild in undisturbed thickets, climbs high into the trees. Introduced into Bermuda. A native of tropical America. Flowers white.

White Morning Glory

Ipomoea alba   Convolvulaceae

Not seen often but a large stand along the grassy cliffs at Willowbank in Somerset.

Madeira Vine

Boussingaultia baselloides   Basellaceae

Seen in undisturbed habitats in thickets of dense growth. Naturalized. A native of South America that has escaped from cultivation. Ovate leaves, long slender raceme with many pale green flowers.

West Indian Cissus

Cissus sicyoides   Vitaceae

Climbing vine with fleshy leaves, flowers umbel-like in clusters. Native. Flowers in the summer and autumn. Seeds possibly brought to Bermuda by birds.

Arrow-Leaved Morning Glory

Ipomoea sagittata   Convolvulaceae

Occasionally seen in marshland habitats. Flowers from spring through autumn. Seeds thought to have reached Bermuda on the wind.

So sweet a kiss the golden sun
gives not to those fresh
morning drops upon the rose.

Loves Labours Lost
Shakespeare

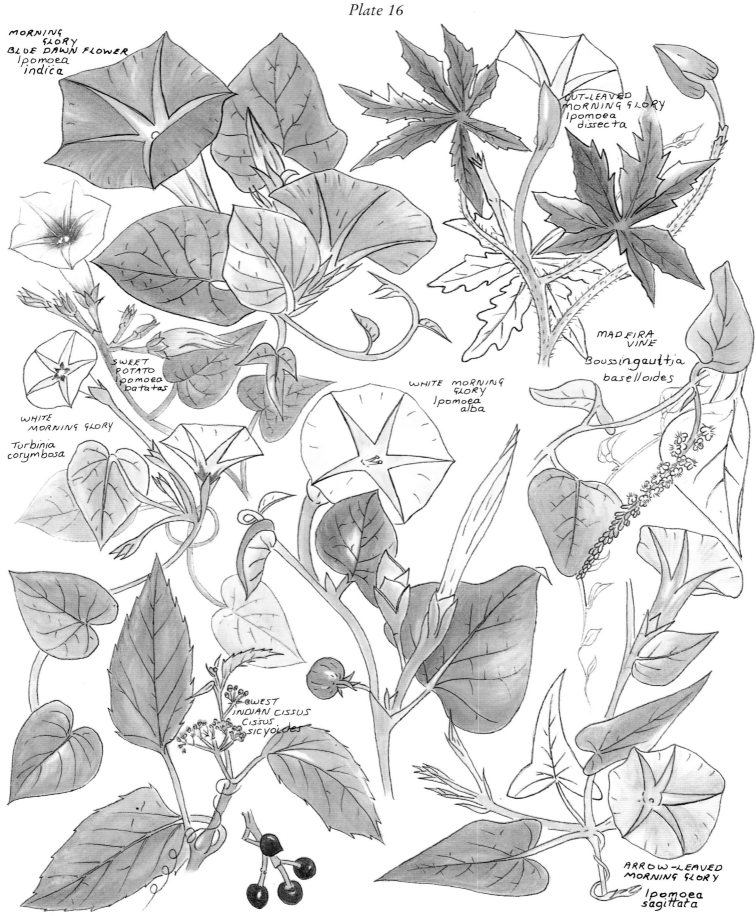

MORNING
GLORY
BLUE DAWN FLOWER
Ipomoea
indica

CUT-LEAVED
MORNING GLORY
Ipomoea
dissecta

MADEIRA
VINE

Boussingaultia
baselloides

SWEET
POTATO
Ipomoea
batatas

WHITE
MORNING GLORY

Turbinia
corymbosa

WHITE MORNING
GLORY
Ipomoea
alba

WEST
INDIAN CISSUS
Cissus
sicyoides

ARROW-LEAVED
MORNING GLORY

Ipomoea
sagittata

Night Blooming Cereus
Hylocereus undatus   Cactaceae
A native of Mexico, this plant has escaped from cultivation and can be seen on thickets in almost any habitat. One of the most dramatic being along the rocks in Somerset, close to the Long Bay beach. Three-winged, fleshy foliage with spines, large white flowers opening at night.

Buddleia
Buddleia madagascariensis   Loganiaceae
This plant has pinnate, oxide, green-grey leaves. Tiny orange star-like flowers. Scrambles through wild areas and untouched roadside copses of trees and shrubs.

Coralita Vine
Antigonon leptopus   Polygonaceae
A vine that climbs with tendrils, originally from Mexico and Colombia. Bright pink flowers. Makes a good garden plant, i.e. on a trellis or tumbling on a hedge or wall.

Pink Trumpet Vine
Podranea ricasoliana   Bignoniaceae
A climbing shrub with pink flowers not unlike those of the white Cedar tree. The throat is white with deep crimson-maroon markings. Blooms in summer to autumn and grows well on or over areas needing a covering to beautify them.

Dutchman's Pipe
Aristolochia littoralis   Aristolochiaceae
Originally from tropical and warm America and Europe. Scrambles over trellis and occasional hedgerows, not commonly seen but a delightful plant. Good example at St George's Historical Society and Elm Lodge Garden in Warwick Parish.

Clematis 'Travellers' Joy'
Clematis flammula   Ranunculaceae
A vine that climbs and twists itself over anything. Found growing in established hedgerows, the distinctive seed has a feathery/hairy appearance and is commonly called 'Old Man's Beard'. This plant came originally from Asia, Europe and North America.

Virginia Creeper
Parthenocissus quinquefolia   Vitaceae
New England to Florida and Texas. Sometimes known also as American Ivy. A vigorous climber in most wild unspoiled areas of Bermuda. Smooth stems with tendrils. Large palmate foliage. Three to five coarsely-toothed green leaflets, glaucous beneath. Turning orange-red in the autumn time. Small red-black berries. One of Bermuda's few autumn colouring subjects. Good for hiding unsightly areas such as newly-built walls.

Chalice Cup Vine
Solandra maxima   Solanaceae
Native of South America. A hardy plant for Bermuda. Large yellow-cream flowers with purple markings in the throat. Very fragrant, up to one foot long. Blooms late summer, tumbles and climbs over other vegetation. Another larger sp. *Gigantium* found growing in the Botanical Gardens. Named after the Swedish botanist Dr Charles Solander, a student of Linnaeus, in the 1700s.

English Ivy
Hedera helix   Araliaceae
Known as the English Ivy but found all through the Northern Hemisphere and also in Australia. A wonderful ground or wall cover, often seen climbing up trees. Its aerial roots will cling to almost anything porous, likes shade.

Passion Flower
Passiflora caerulea   Passifloraceae
Named passion flower from the Latin 'Passio' and 'floris' because of the parts' resemblance to the crucifixion. Grows in many gardens in sheltered areas. The local perfume factory has a whole field for use in making the perfume. Climbs on tendrils.

And each flower and herb on
Earth's dark breast
Rose from the dreams of its
wintery rest.

Shelley

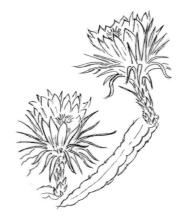

NIGHT BLOOMING **CEREUS**
Hylocereus
undatus

BUDDLEIA
Buddleia
madagascariensis

DUTCHMAN'S
PIPE
Aristolochia
littoralis

PINK
TRUMPET
VINE
Podranea
ricasoliana

CORALITA
VINE
Antigonon
leptopus

TRAVELLERS
JOY
Clematis
flammula

CHALICE CUP
VINE
Solandra
maxima

PASSION
FLOWER
Passiflora
caerulea

VIRGINIA
CREEPER
Parthenocissus
quinquefolia

ENGLISH
IVY
Hedera
helix

Creeping Fig
Ficus pumila   Moraceae
A tiny, woody climber related to the Indian Rubber tree. Seems to put out two kinds of growth, tiny leaves that cling to walls, leathery green foliage and aerial roots and also larger leaves that grow more erect and do not climb as much.

Purple Passion
Setcreasea purpurea   Commelinaceae
Known also as the Silvery Wandering Jew of Mexico. Two varieties, silvery-green and purplish-green, seem to thrive in Bermuda. Quite succulent and pretty, delicate rosy flowers. Very fleshy and trailing, rooting at its joints. Small ovate leaves. Good for ground cover locally.

Wandering Jew
Tradescantia fluminensis   Commelinaceae
Planted for ornamental ground cover, sometimes found in more wild habitats. Native of the West Indies and Central America. Leaves purple beneath and green-purple on the face, rose-coloured flowers.

Yellow Japanese Honeysuckle
Lonicera japonica   Caprifoliaceace
The most fragrant of the three honeysuckles found in Bermuda, a common English hedge plant. It twines itself into a nice hedge plant over a fence or wall. Its creamy-white tubular flowers turn pale orange soon after opening. Flowering June time.

Wedelia
Wedelia trilobata   Compositae
Originally from the West Indies and North and South America. Internationally known as the 'Creeping Daisy'. Used an enormous amount locally for ground cover. A fast grower, with slender flexible trailing stems. Bright, shining green leaves, slightly fleshy. Bright yellow flowers with golden-brown florets.

Palm Grass
Setaria palmifolia   Graminae
One of the more vigorous members of the grass family, well suited for ground cover planting in shaded areas. The botanical gardens have excellent examples. The sword-like, dark green leaves look similar to young emerging palm fronds growing to 4 feet in length. Flowering spikes grow up to 6 feet in length. A very attractive plant not suited for small gardens as it spreads and will become invasive. Palm Grass is propagated by division, done during the winter months.

Queen of the Night
Selenicereus grandiflorus   Cactaceae
Seen planted in gardens and climbing over walls, the round prickly stems climb with aerial roots, it has nocturnal flowers. The stems for this species are quite dramatically different from the stems of its sister plant the Night Blooming Cereus. The flowers attract a nocturnal moth that pollinates it.

King's Mantle
Thunbergia erecta   Acanthaceae
An evergreen deciduous shrub from tropical Africa. Trumpet-shaped violet flowers lobed, with a yellow throat. Thin ovate leaves. Flowers from spring to autumn.

Ice Plant
Carpobrotus edulis   Aizoaceae
A succulent, often planted for ground cover in Bermuda – mostly sandy and seashore areas. Branching, with fleshy leaves, pink flowers with yellow stamens. Originally from South Pacific – the Cape Peninsula.

Thunbergia (Purple Allamanda)
Thunbergia grandiflora   Acanthaceae
Found flowering in spring to autumn. Trailing woody vine, short stalked leaf, up to 8 inch long spear, 3-5 veigned from base. Toothed/lobed lilac flowers with cream throat about 3 inches long and wide. A white variety can be found.

So doth the woodbine
The sweet honeysuckle
Gently entwist.

Midsummer Night's Dream
Shakespeare

YELLOW JAPANESE
HONEY SUCKLE
Lonicera
Japonica

PURPLE
PASSION
Setcreasea
purpurea

CREEPING
FIG
Ficus pumila

WANDERING
JEW
Tradescantia
fluminensis

QUEEN
OF THE
NIGHT

Selenicereus
grandiflorus

PALM
GRASS
Setaria
palmifolia

WEDELIA
Wedelia
trilobata

KING'S
MANTLE
Thunbergia
erecta

ICE PLANT
Carpobrotus
edulis

THUNBERGIA
- PURPLE ALLAMANDA
Thunbergia grandiflora

19 Tropical plants and vines

Pigeon Berry
Duranta erecta (syn. *Duranta repens*)   Verbenaceae
Naturalized. A native of Florida, the West Indies and tropical America. Frequently planted as a garden ornamental small tree. It has tiny pale purple flowers followed by bright orange berries.

Allamanda
Allamanda cathartica   Apocynaceae
Flowers mid-summer through autumn, the bright yellow flowers and dark green leaves scramble their way over walls or other neighbouring plants. Originally from South America and Brazil. Sometimes called the golden trumpet.

Trumpet Honeysuckle
Lonicera sempervirens   Caprifoliaceae
A climbing vine, planted mostly as a garden ornamental plant. The oval leaves are a paler green beneath. Yellow-scarlet tubular flowers in clusters. It can sometimes escape into the hedgerow flora and is seen in quite wild locations.

Sleeping Hibiscus (Wax Mallow or Turks Cap)
Malvaviscus arboreus   Malvaceae
Native of Mexico, sometimes called Scotchman's Purse. Grows islandwide. Resembles the Hibiscus when it is closed in the day, but in fact, the bright red flowers never open. Used often as a hedging plant. Its evergreen foliage is slightly more yellow than the common Hibiscus. There is also a pink form which is less commonly seen.

Cape Honeysuckle
Tecomaria capensis   Bignoniaceae
A scrambling shrub, originally from South Africa. Flowers bright orange with spotted throat in the corolla. Known sometimes as the trumpet flower, it is planted widely as a hedgerow plant. An evergreen that has become naturalized.

Barbados Gooseberry
Pereskia aculeata   Cactaceae
Found in tropical America, a spiny vine that usually climbs high, tumbling through dense thickets of vegetation. Oval leaves and large clusters of flowers, white, very fragrant, followed by leafy, edible, yellowish-orange berries. I have noticed from the vine in my garden that it seems to flower for just one day of the year in summertime.

Hibiscus
Hibiscus rosa sinensis   Malvaceae
Flowers white to yellow to red, often maroon spots on petals' edge. Warm temperate to tropical. In tropical America used for shining shoes. Often cultivated under glass in temperate regions.

Blue Pea
Clitoria ternata   Leguminosae
Cultivated and found in established protected gardens. Originally from the East Indies. Bright blue flowers with a yellow throat. The seed case, like a pea pod, is quite hairy.

Blue Plumbago
Plumbago auriculata   Plumbaginaceae
The sky-blue flowers have sticky hairs at their base. Flowers all through the summer into the winter months. Will sprawl if allowed. Known locally as the sticker plant as it easily sticks to clothes and animals.

Ink Berry (Small Passion Flower)
Passiflora suberosa   Passifloraceae
Seen occasionally on walls and shady areas in very old established gardens. Seen in its pure wild state at Nonsuch Island. Often found in old gardens on steps or under shrubs and trees that are left untouched. Should be more cherished and propagated. The tiny green flowers are a delight, the berries are deep purple-black.

Jasmine
Jasminum simplicifolium   Oleaceae
Common in Castle Harbour jungle areas, the woody vine climbs through trees forming dense thickets. Dark green, shiny leaves and white, very fragrant flowers – used for local jasmine perfume production.

Bougainvillea
Bougainvillea glabra   Nyctaginaceae
The vibrant flowers of this plant are in fact 'bracts' or modified leaves. If you look closely you will notice the flowers are tiny and white. It tends to sprawl and twist over whatever it finds in its path. Can be trained on trelliswork – thrives in protected areas.

Cat's Claw Vine
Macfadyena unguis-cati   Bignoniaceae
Found growing on walls, in hedgerows. Sometimes seen enveloping a tree, up to 40 feet. Cascading branches with yellow flowers. Anthers eject pollen explosively.

Roving Sailor
Maurandya erubescens   Scrophulariaceae
Native of south-west USA and Mexico. Flowers from spring to autumn, slender climbing plant, not at all common. Seen in Walsingham Jungle and also thrives when planted on shady hedgerows. Leaves triangular, pink flowers with corolla tube lilac-pink with white at throat. This, and also the smaller lilac species, have originated from a garden escape and naturalized.

Climbing Foxglove
Maurandya scandens   Scrophulariaceae
Native of Mexico. Found growing along banks and hedges throughout the wilder areas of the Islands. Flowers all through the summer. Similar to the other climbing Foxglove yet a very much larger form; is quite hairy. Flowers tiny, the corolla is pale lilac with white and yellow inner tube.

The poetry of the Earth is never dead.

Keats

PIGEON BERRY
Duranta erecta

ALLAMANDA
Allamanda cathartica

TRUMPET HONEYSUCKLE
Lonicera sempervirens

CAPE HONESUCHLE
Tecomaria capensis

BARBADOS GOOSEBERRY
Pereskia aculeata

HIBISCUS
Rosa sinensis

SLEEPING HIBISCUS
TURKS CAP
Malvaviscus arboreus

CATS CLAW VINE
Macfadyena unguis-cati

BLUE PLUMBAGO
Plumbago auriculata

BLUE PEA
Clitoria ternata

JASMINE
Jasminum simplicifolium

INK BERRY
Passiflora suberosa

ROVING SAILOR
Maurandya erubescens

BOUGAINVILLEA
Bougainvillea glabra

CLIMBING FOXGLOVE
Maurandya scandens

Elm-Leaved Begonia
Begonia ulmifolia   Begoniaceae
Native of Trinidad and South America. Can be seen occasionally in dry stone walls. Tiny white-pink flowers.

Lace Plant (Artillery Plant)
Pilea microphylla   Urticaceae
Naturalized from the West Indies. Native of south Florida and tropical America. Planted in gardens but mostly seen along roadside walls and waste ground.

Yellow Atamasco Lily
Zephyranthes atamasco   Liliaceae
From Cuba. Occasionally seen in garden grassland and along unmown roadside verges.

Purple Atamasco Lily
Zephyranthes atamasco   Liliaceae
Native of south-east USA. Flowers in the spring, sometimes autumn. All the Atamasco Lilies seem to be scarce, they have escaped from cultivation and are likely to multiply.

White Atamasco Lily
Zephyranthes atamasco 'Album'   Liliaceae
Native of tropical America, the pale purple flowers appear in the spring and summer.

Speckled Kalanchoe
Kalanchoe tubiflora   Crassulaceae
Found growing in rocky hedgerows and gardens. Tiny pink flowers growing in clusters. Old name Bryophyllum.

Kalanchoe
Kalanchoe flammea   Crassulaceae
Seen occasionally in gardens. Flowering in early summertime.

Gaillardia Firewheels
Gaillardia pulchella   Compositae
A low-growing, attractive ground cover plant which has become naturalized and established in the Mullet Bay Park area of St George's and West Side Road in Somerset. A hardy plant introduced from north-west USA, and seen in many areas. Striking foliage and yellow-orange flowers, its leaves are formed in basal rosettes.

Gazania
Gazania ringens var. *uniflora*   Compositae
A garden escape found growing on dry hillside slopes and rocky outcrops in sandy soil. Leaves hairy.

Madagascar Periwinkle
Catharanthus roseus   Apocynaceae
From Java to Brazil. Madagascar periwinkle, fleshy plant with oblong leaves. Flowers white or rosy red. A very popular garden plant.

Shrimp Plant
Justicia brandegeana   Acanthaceae
(syn. *Beloperone guttata*)
From Mexico, wiry stems with ovate hairy leaves. Red-brownish bracts with white flowers showing beneath, showing tiny purple markings. Appearance: terminal spikes hanging downwards.

Geranium (Zonal Pelargonium)
Pelargonium x. hortorum   Geraniaceae
Originally from Africa, many varieties grow well in Bermuda. Scented geranium, also seen frequently in gardens.

False Garlic
Nothoscordum gracile   Liliaceae
Found on waste and cultivated ground. Naturalized in southern USA and Jamaica. Native of Africa. Flowers in spring and summer. Umbel of white flowers. Pop up often in gardens and lawns.

In the great gardens,
after spring rain,
We find sweet innocence
come once again.

Edith Sitwell

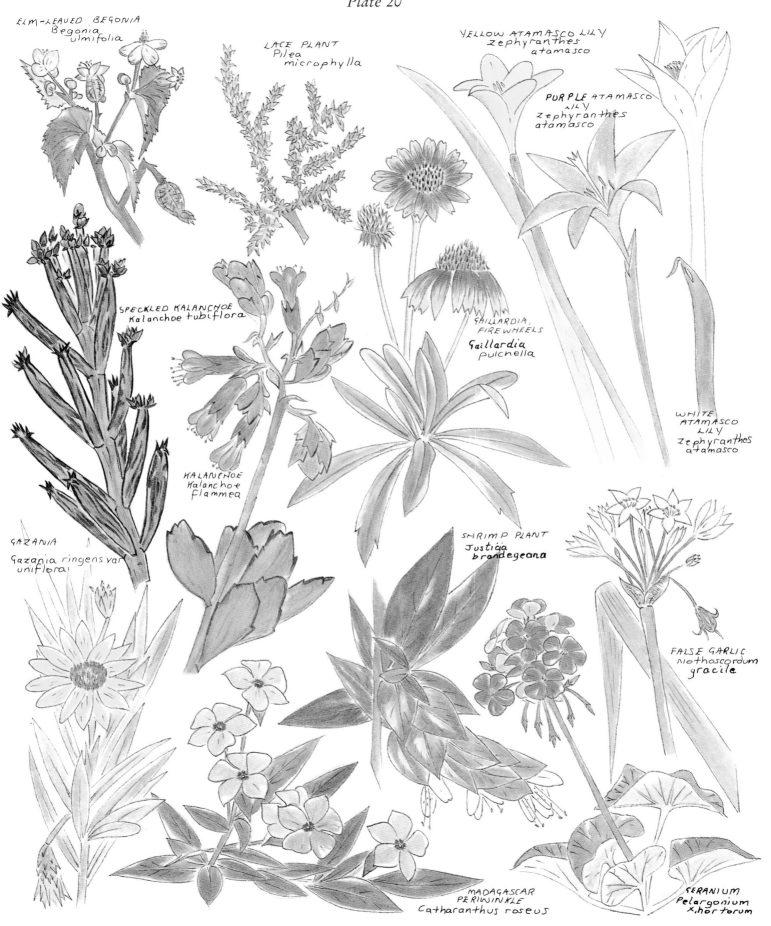

ELM-LEAVED BEGONIA
Begonia
ulmifolia

LACE PLANT
Pilea
microphylla

YELLOW ATAMASCO LILY
zephyranthes
atamasco

PURPLE ATAMASCO
LILY
zephyranthes
atamasco

SPECKLED KALANCHOE
Kalanchoe tubiflora

GAILLARDIA,
FIREWHEELS
Gaillardia
pulchella

WHITE
ATAMASCO
LILY
Zephyranthes
atamasco

KALANCHOE
Kalanchoe
flammea

GAZANIA
Gazania ringens var.
uniflora

SHRIMP PLANT
Justicia
brandegeana

FALSE GARLIC
Nothoscordum
gracile

MADAGASCAR
PERIWINKLE
Catharanthus roseus

GERANIUM
Pelargonium
X.hortorum

Corn Flag Gladiolus

Gladiolus italicus　　　　　　　　　　　　　Iridaceae
Escaped from gardens, seen growing wild on hillsides, waste and cultivated land, growing up to 2 feet high.

Day Lily

Hemerocallis fulva　　　　　　　　　　　　　Liliaceae
Originally from Europe. Long leaves with clusters of pale, orange-yellow flowers, opening for a day. Once established are good as spreading, ground cover plants. Popular in gardens.

African Blue Lily

Agapanthus africanus　　　　　　　　　　　　Liliaceae
From the Cape of Good Hope. Flowers all through the summer, its bright blue flowers bring the sky down to earth's level. Planted frequently in gardens to add a splash of colour in formal border designs. A large 3 inch umbel, on tall erect stalks, adds great diversity of form to any garden.

Canna Lily (Red)

Canna indica　　　　　　　　　　　　　　　Cannaceae
Native to tropical America, found growing in cultivation and on waste ground. Leaves oblong and elliptic, with dark red markings on the deep red leaf. Flowers on spikes, bright red with reddish-yellow tip.

Spider Lily

Hymenocallis caribaea　　　　　　　　　　Amaryyllidaceae
Naturalized. Native of the West Indies. White flowers that appear in the spring and autumn. A popular plant for gardens, also sometimes seen in mass plantings along roadsides. An example of this is along the south shore in Warwick.

Crinum Lily

Crinum angustum　　　　　　　　　　　　Amaryllidaceae
The crinum lily is a popular garden plant that can also be seen growing in isolated places such as the beach at Fricks Point in Tuckers Town.

Bermuda Easter Lily

Lilium longiflorum (var. *ensiforme*)　　　　　Liliaceae
This plant was once grown on the Bermuda Islands for export. Today such quantities are not possible mostly because arable land is not as plentiful. The very beautiful flowers are very fragrant, so much so that a perfume has been created at the local perfume factory. Flowering time: spring-early summer. Flowers sent to H.M. Queen Elizabeth every Eastertime.

Arrowroot

Maranta arundinacea　　　　　　　　　　　Marantaceae
Arrowroot was once a major crop in Bermuda, also the islands of St Vincent. Native to tropical America, tiny white flowers in summertime. Root has a popular starch much used in French cooking, acting as a thickening agent with less carbohydrate than normal cooking starch. Stems 2-3 feet tall, leaves long and much veined.

Canna Lily (Yellow)

Canna generalis　　　　　　　　　　　　　Cannaceae
Native to tropical America. Bright yellow flowers with orange spotted markings. Not frequently seen but a lovely ornamental plant.

Calla Lily (White)

Zantedeschia aethiopica　　　　　　　　　　Araceae
South and North Africa, known as White Calla or Arum Lily. Glossy green leaves, quite succulent. Stout stalk bearing a large, funnel-shaped, rolled, waxy-white spathe, surrounding a bright yellow spadix. It is apparently common to see fields in bloom in South Africa in the summertime.

Bird of Paradise

Strelitzia reginae　　　　　　　　　　　Stretliziaceae
Originally from South Africa, many gardens in Bermuda grow this lovely plant. Very stiff in appearance with bright orange flowers with blue stamen parts. Flowers form in an arrow-shaped pink-green case. The whole appearance is like that of an exotic bird.

Shell Ginger (Zingiber)

Alpinia zerumbet 'Varigata'　　　　　　　Zingiberaceae
Native of Eastern Asia, a popular garden plant on the Islands. Grows up to and sometimes seen over 12 feet. Flowers very fragrant and smell of ginger, a pendulous spike, pale pink with bright crimson markings. Given plenty of room it will spread well. Majority of this group of herbs are grown for their rhizomes.

A flower is to be watched
as it grows
in its association with the earth,
the air and the dew.
Its leaves are to be seen
as they expand
in the sunshine.
Its colours as they embroider
the field
or illuminate the forest.

Ruskin

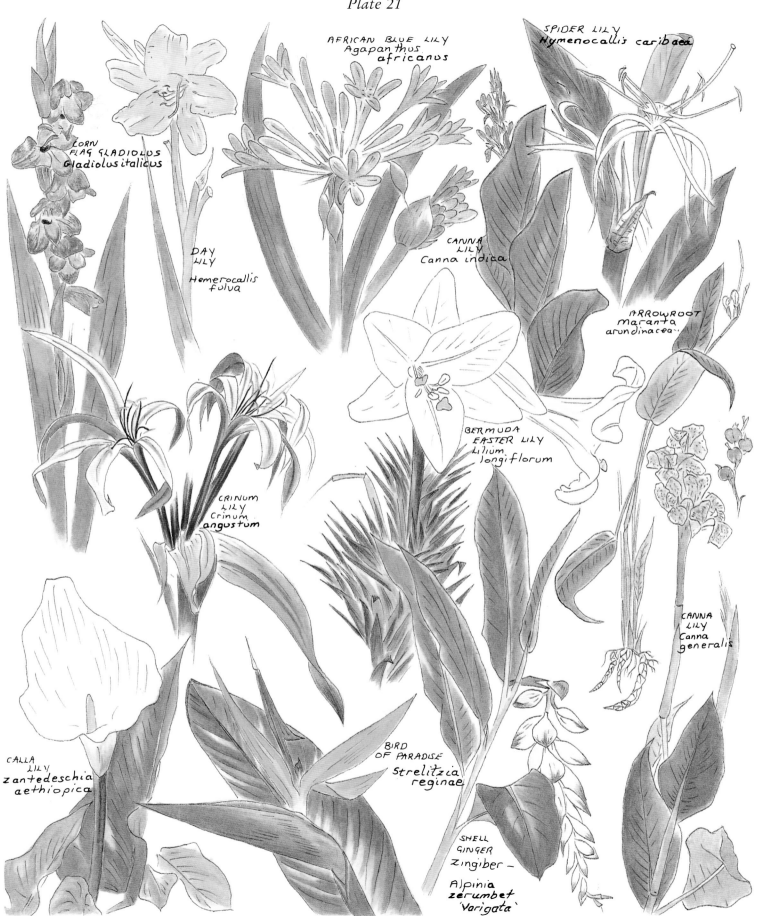

LORN
FLAG GLADIOLUS
Gladiolus italicus

AFRICAN BLUE LILY
Agapanthus
africanus

SPIDER LILY
Hymenocallis caribaea

DAY
LILY

Hemerocallis
fulva

CANNA
LILY
Canna indica

ARROWROOT
maranta
arundinacea

CRINUM
LILY
Crinum
angustum

BERMUDA
EASTER LILY
Lilium
longiflorum

CANNA
LILY
Canna
generalis

CALLA
LILY
zantedeschia
aethiopica

BIRD
OF PARADISE
Strelitzia
reginae

SHELL
GINGER
Zingiber –

Alpinia
zerumbet
'Varigata'

Snow Bush

Breynia nivosa 'Variegata'   Euphorbiaceae
Originally from the South Sea Islands, a hedge bush. Green, mottled variegated leaves with white-pink mottled markings at tips and delicate pink variegated cups that look like flowers on the red stems.

Spicy Jatropha

Jatropha integerrima   Euphorbiaceae
From Central America. Large lobed leaves with scarlet flowers, seen growing in many gardens.

Lady of the Night

Brunfelsia americana   Solanaceae
From the West Indies, an evergreen shrub with fairly leathery leaves. Flowers cream fading to yellow, very fragrant especially at night, form is a tubular shape with petals attached.

Match me if you can

Acalypha wilkesiana   Euphorbiaceae
Many varieties of Acalypha grow in Bermuda but the variegated copper leaf and greens are most commonly seen. Mostly from the South Sea Islands. Colour variations are beautiful and many find fun in trying in vain to match two of a kind.

Croton

Codiaeum variegatum   Euphorbiaceae
Bermuda has many varieties of Crotons. They are tropical ornamental shrubs that have a variety of colours and forms of thick leathery leaves. Evergreen, and originally from Polynesia. Mostly always variegated with yellow, red and green and other mottled colours. A good hedge plant and also a colourful border plant.

Cassava Manihot

Manihot utilissima   Euphorbiaceae
Native of South America, widely cultivated in the West Indies and grown in Bermuda for its edible tubers which yield a starch that is made into a delicious pie at Christmas time. It is quite bitter and poisonous until cooked, resembles tapioca, almond fragrance. Leaves deeply parted in 3-7 lobes. Two years needed to wait for root tubers to reach maturity.

Crown of Thorns

Euphorbia milii var. *splendens*   Euphorbiaceae
From west Madagascar, a shrub with many spines and slender woody stems, branches also have spines, leaves deciduous. Flower bracts are soft red with pale centre and can be trained to grow on a trellis. Fairly commonly seen, seems to flower most of the year.

Butterfly Gardenia

Tabernaemontana divaricata   Apocynaceae
From India, white flowers, glossy green leaves, more fragrant at night. Blooms in summertime. An attractive shrub not often planted locally.

Mock Orange or Orange Jessamine

Murraya paniculata   Rutaceae
Evergreen leathery leaves, loves tropical climates. Very fragrant flowers. Planted in many gardens, it makes a good hedge plant.

Poinsettia

Euphorbia pulcherrima   Euphorbiaceae
Used as a Christmas pot plant all over the world, originally from Mexico. Locally adds colour to many gardens. Very tropical looking with its bright red bracts standing out in many private garden settings. They are usually at their best for the Christmas season.

Knowst thou the land where the pale Citrons grow,
The golden fruits in darker foliage glow?
Soft blows the wind that breathes from that blue sky.

Coleridge

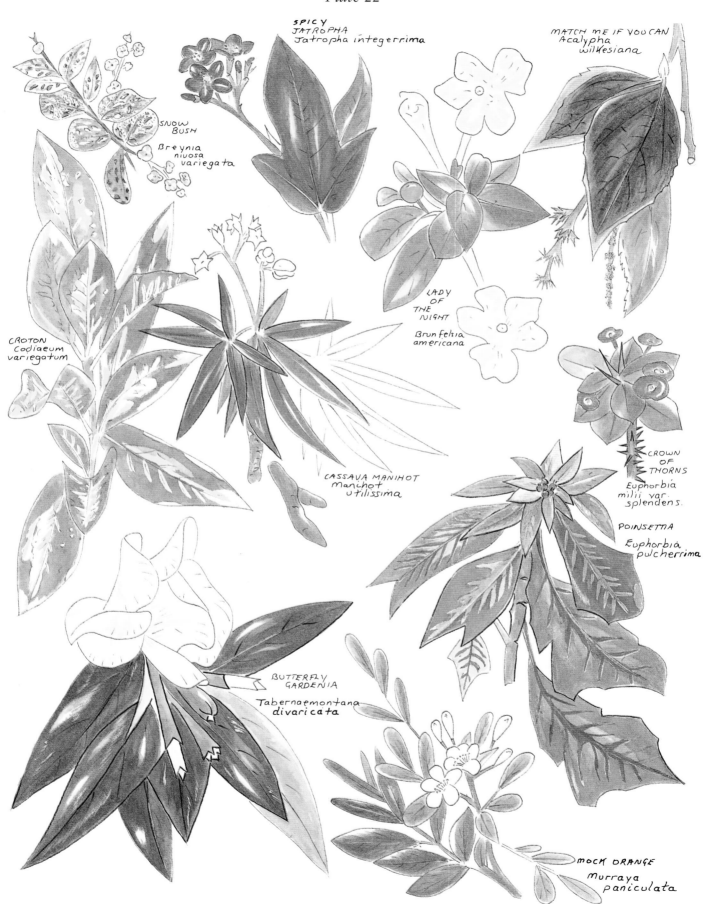

SPICY
JATROPHA
Jatropha integerrima

MATCH ME IF YOU CAN
Acalypha
wilkesiana

SNOW
BUSH

Breynia
nivosa
variegata

CROTON
Codiaeum
variegatum

LADY
OF
THE
NIGHT

Brunfelsia
americana

CROWN
OF
THORNS

Euphorbia
milii var.
splendens.

CASSAVA MANIHOT
Manihot
utilissima

POINSETTIA

Euphorbia
pulcherrima

BUTTERFLY
GARDENIA

Tabernaemontana
divaricata

MOCK ORANGE

Murraya
paniculata

Umbrella Plant
Cyperus alternifolius   Cyperaceae
Clustering perennial bog plant with ribbed stalks to 3 feet
high, with a crown of bright green, grass-like leaves around a
head of small, green flowers. Found also in gardens.

Tree Dracaena
Dracaena arborea   Liliaceae
Dense head of broad, sword-shaped leaves. Seen in garden
habitat. Roots of Dracaenas orange-yellow.

Cochineal Cactus
Opuntia cochenillifera   Cactaceae
A smooth, flat-jointed shining cactus commonly seeding in
gardens. In tropical America, where this cactus originated, it is
the support plant to the mealybug that furnishes cochineal dye.
New family name 'Nopalea'.

Cow Cane or Giant Reed
Arundo donax   Gramineae
Found in Mediterranean, naturalized in the southern USA. A
very large grass that looks like a fine bamboo. Woody stems
with flat grey-green leaves. Inflorescence in slender greenish-
purple plumes.

Bamboo Cane 'Bambusa'
Gigantochola vertiallata   Gramineae
Found in dense thickets mostly in old established gardens. The
main stem is so strong that the same species has been used for
building purposes such as scaffolding. The leaves have a pink-
orange tint and grow on tiny branches.

Yellow Nut Grass
Cyperus esculentus   Cyperaceae
Seen occasionally islandwide. Flowers in the summer months.
A very attractive plant.

Great American Bullrush
Schoenoplectus vallidus   Cyperaceae
Umbrella sedge found in marshes on edges of cultivated land
and also on roadsides. Flower heads made up of spikelets of
scales, yellowish-brown. Short, tuber root stalks.

Giant False Agave
Furcraea gigantea   Amaryllidaceae
From Brazil, rosette-like with a high branched inflorescence,
milk-white flowers.

Agave (Century Plant 'Yellow Edge')
Agave americana marginata   Agavaceae
Though erroneous, the belief is that Agaves flower only when
100 years old, but in fact it is more like 10-20 years. Bermuda's
rather tropical look owes much to the many Agaves and Aloes
that grow on her shores.

Madagascar Dragon Tree
Dracaena marginata   Liliaceae
Tree-like, with branching slender trunk growing up to 16 feet
high. The top has a dense terminal rosette of thick, fleshy
leaves.

Century Plant (Green)
Agave americana   Agavaceae
The most commonly seen Agave. Yellow flowers at the top of
a spike of up to 30 feet high. The marginata sp. is the
variegated form, originally from Mexico.

Aloe Bitter
Aloe succotrina   Liliaceae
There are several Aloes on the Islands. Aloes are succulent
plants. This species grows up to 3-4 feet high, and has
branching stems. Its leaves look slightly glaucous. Flowers
small, red spikes. A very decorative border plant.

Agave Sisal Hemp
Agave sisalana   Agavaceae
Originally from Mexico's Yucatan Peninsula. There are several
species of Agave in Bermuda, locally referred to as Century
Plants. In Mexico it is grown for rope (sisal).

True Aloe
Aloe vera   Liliaceae
This is the most famous of Aloes because its pulp has become
well known for its many medicinal uses and cures. Commonly
used now for sunburn and cosmetic creams. Flowers are
yellow and branch out on a stem in a nodding form.

Aloe sp.   Liliaceae
Occasionally seen in park or garden habitats, sending up a
large, cascading flower spike 6-8 feet long.

Candelabra Aloe
Aloe arborescens   Liliaceae
Spreading rosette with sword-like, fleshy, tapering leaves. Seen
islandwide. Orange-yellow flowers.

Century Plant (Grey)
Agave americana var. *barbadensis*   Agavaceae
From southern USA to tropical South America. It has a
spectacular, fast-growing inflorescence.

Canoe Plant
Rhoeo discolor   Commelinaceae
Origin Mexico. Fleshy stems 8 inches long, branching at the
base, dark green above and purple beneath. Little white
flowers. Becoming popular as a bedding plant locally.

One month is past, another
is begun
Since merry bells rang out the
dying year,
And buds of rarest green began
to peer,
As if impatient for a
warmer sun.

H. Coleridge, 1842

UMBRELLA PLANT
Cyperus alternifolius

TREE DRACAENA
Dracaena arborea

YELLOW NUT GRASS
Cyperus esculentis

COCHINEAL CACTUS
Opuntia cochenillifera

COW CANE
Arundo donax

BAMBOO CANE
'Bambusa'
Gigantochola vertiallata

AGAVE
Agave americana marginata

MADAGASCAR DRAGON TREE
Dracaena marginata

GIANT FALSE AGAVE
Furcraea gigantea

GREAT AMERICAN BULLRUSH
Schoenoplectus vallidus

CENTURY PLANT GREEN
Agave americana

ALOE BITTER
Aloe succotrina

AGAVE SISAL HEMP
Agave sisalana

TRUE ALOE
Aloe vera

CANOE PLANT
Rhoeo discolor

CANDELABRA ALOE
Aloe arborescens

ALOE SP.

CENTURY PLANT GREY
Agave americana var. barbadensis

Sago Palm

Cycas circinalis   Cycadaceae
Originally from India, Madagascar and New Guinea.
Sometimes known as the fern palm. The Sago Palms' stout
trunk has a rosette of stiff leaves. Male and female
inflorescence on separate plants. Although not true palms,
cycads are often classed with the palm family.

Sago Palm (Japanese)

Cycas revoluta   Cycadaceae
First seen in Japan and Java, a palm-like tree with a stout trunk
and branching stiff, green pinnate leaves. Fruit found in a fur-
like hairy case at crown, seed bright orange. Cycads are some
of the oldest known plants to man – many surviving from
families originating in prehistoric times.

Screw Palm

Pandanus utilis   Pandanaceae
Found first in Madagascar. A lovely tree on the landscape, its
typical spiral rosettes of long, strap-like leathery leaves are
deep to pale olive-green tones. Forms stilt-like roots. Foliage
often used to make baskets. Although sometimes called a
screw pine it is neither a pine nor palm. Can be planted in
exposed positions as in Mangrove Bay, Somerset. Prefers sandy
soils.

Traveller's Tree

Ravenala madagascariensis   Strelitziaceae
A lovely tree with palm-like trunks and leathery banana-like
leaves, in a fan shape arch when mature. The flowers are fleshy
cases of deep purple with white and sky blue petals. Looks like
a tropical bird (as Strelitzia).

With light and butterfly
the world did seem
to flicker and flint,
As if the maker slept in a dream
imagined it.

SAGO PALM
Cycas circinalis

SAGO PALM
Cycas revoluta

SCREW PALM
Pandanus utilis

TRAVELLER'S TREE
Ravenala madagascariensis

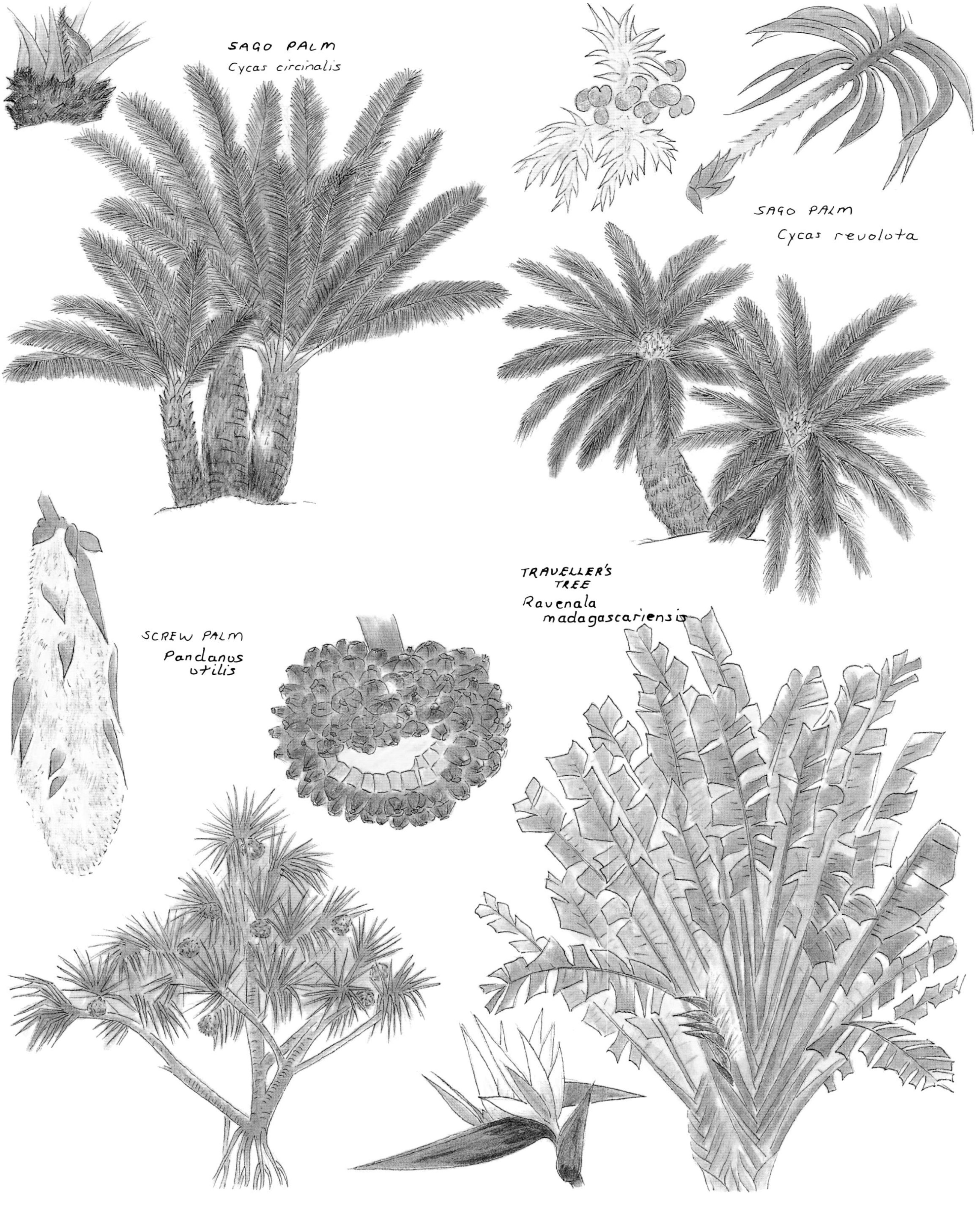

Fishtail Palm

Caryota urens   Palmae

Originated from Himalayas – India, Burma, Ceylon and Malaya. The Fishtail grows in a few gardens. It has branching stems and sends up new shoots when one stem dies. Known also as the wine palm. Bipinnate arching leaves with thick, wedge-shaped, loosely-spread segments. Yields wine. Tropical.

Bottle Palm

Hyophorbe lagenicaulis   Palmae

From the Islands. Bottle Palm grows in a few gardens and parks. Its leaves twist and have a typical swollen shape at the base, where the trunk bulges and tapers into a normal upright shape. The top crown holds a few stiff pinnate arching fronds. Almost extinct in the wild having been reduced to nine trees in Mauritius.

Lady Palm

Rhapis excelsa   Palmae

The Lady Palm has multiple trunks that are very narrow. Its appearance is like a dwarf bamboo only dark brown with beige rings. Leaves are pale green. Forms clumps from underground suckers. Leathery leaves, divided into 3-10 broad segments.

Spindle Palm

Hyophorbe verschaffeltii   Palmae

More commonly seen than the closely related Bamboo Palm, differs with craggy tough silvery trunk which curves in the shape of a spindle. Grows up to 20 feet. Leaves stout, slightly arching flowers, white, produced just below the crown shaft. Fruits reddish turning dark purple. Grows easily from seed. Young plants distinguished by a marked triangular stem.

Dwarf Date Palm

Phoenix roebelenii   Palmae

Assam to Vietnam. Pigmy Date Palm. This plant is not found often but is tidy and elegant. The grey-green leaves fold slightly. It grows up to 8 feet high. Native of Florida. Fruit berry-like, in large clusters.

Solitaire Palm

Ptychosperma elegans   Palmae

Originating from Queensland, Australia. The Solitaire Palm has a thin trunk with a slightly wider base. It has dark grey rings on the trunk's surface. The leaves are pleated with rather short, pinnate fronds. It grows up to 16 feet and seems very hardy. Bushy, white-red fruits. Tropical.

I wandered lonely as a cloud
That floats on high o'er Vales
and Hills.
When all at once I saw a crowd
A host of dancing Daffodils,
Along the lake beneath the trees
Ten thousand dancing in
the breeze.

William Wordsworth

FISHTAIL PALM
Caryota urens

BOTTLE PALM
Hyophorbe lagenicaulis

LADY PALM *Rhapis excelsa*

SOLITAIRE PALM

Ptychosperma elegans

DWARF DATE PALM
Phoenix roebelenii

SPINDLE PALM
Hyophorbe verschaffeltii

Coconut Palm

Cocos nucifera   Palmae

Widely spread into all tropical regions (Indian archipelago). Single trunk with rather swollen base, normal curves. Pale brown-beige trunk with ring scars. Fibre forms a matting material at leaf stem. The leaves are stiff and orange-green in appearance. The fruit takes 12 months to mature and is often not edible in Bermuda, although it is possible to have some milk and flesh.

Date Palm

Phoenix dactylifera   Palmae

Originates in Arabia-Africa and has descendants in Californian deserts. Date Palms are not often seen on Bermuda. They fruit but mostly do not mature enough to eat. Leaves are very stiff and have fine powder on.

Senegal Date

Phoenix reclinata   Palmae

Found in tropical Africa from Senegal to Natal. Not often seen, produces many trunks. The leaves are quite spiny and dark green. Grows quite tall, 40 feet high.

Bamboo Palm or Butterfly Palm

Chrysalidocarpus lutescens   Palmae

Originally from Madagascar, this palm is branching and extremely attractive. The leaves are bright green with golden-yellow stems. The trunks are sectioned and grooved with the same subtle colourings as the foliage, forming clumps 26 feet tall. Fruit when ripe becomes a violet-black.

Canary Island Date Palm

Phoenix canariensis   Palmae

Single trunk, mostly wider at the top. Leaves tend to hold on and become dense. Ferms often grow on the trunk's fibrous growth. Flower stalks are orange. The fruit may be eaten but rarely is on Bermuda. Plants widely found in sub-tropical regions.

Oh, could you view
the scenery dear,
That now beneath
my window lies,
You'd think that nature
lavished here
Her purest wave, her
softest skies.

Tom Moore

COCONUT PALM
Cocos
nucifera

DATE PALM
Phoenix
dactylifera

SENEGAL
DATE
Phoenix
reclinata

BAMBOO OR BUTTERFLY
PALM
Chrysalidocarpus
lutescens

CANARY ISLAND
DATE PALM
Phoenix
canariensis

27 Ornamental palms

Cuban Royal Palm
Roystonea regia   Palmae
The Royal Palm is originally from Cuba. The fruit is pale purple and elongated. The trunk is pale grey-beige and it is the most grand of all palms growing in Bermuda. A typical form has swollen growth above the middle, grows over 20 feet high. The arching, feathery fronds are regularly pinnate and arranged in double rows in two planes on either side of axis.

Princess Palm
Dictyosperma album   Palmae
From Mauritius, this palm has a very distinctive leaf shape that is dark yet glaucous in colour. The trunk is grey and fairly smooth. The flowers are red-yellow and the seed head's stem system is very ornate and like an exotic comb when dried.

Washingtonia Palm
Washingtonia filifera   Palmae
Originating in south California desert, Arizon, and Baja, California. A dramatic plant which has a skirt of dried leaves showing under the green leaf foliage of the crown. The trunk is pale brown. Known throughout the world as the Desert Fan Palm or Petticoat Palm.

Queen Palm
Arecastrum romanzoffianum (syn. Syagrus romanzoffianus)   Palmae
Originally from Bahai to Argentina and Bolivia. This palm has a straight trunk, with a graceful crown of long, arching leaf fronds. Has edible orange fruit that will not mature in Bermuda's sub-tropical climate.

A birdie with a yellow bill
Hopped upon the window sill,
Cocked his shining eye and said
'Aint you shamed you
sleepy head!'

Robert Louis Stevenson

ORNAMENTAL PALMS

Plate 27

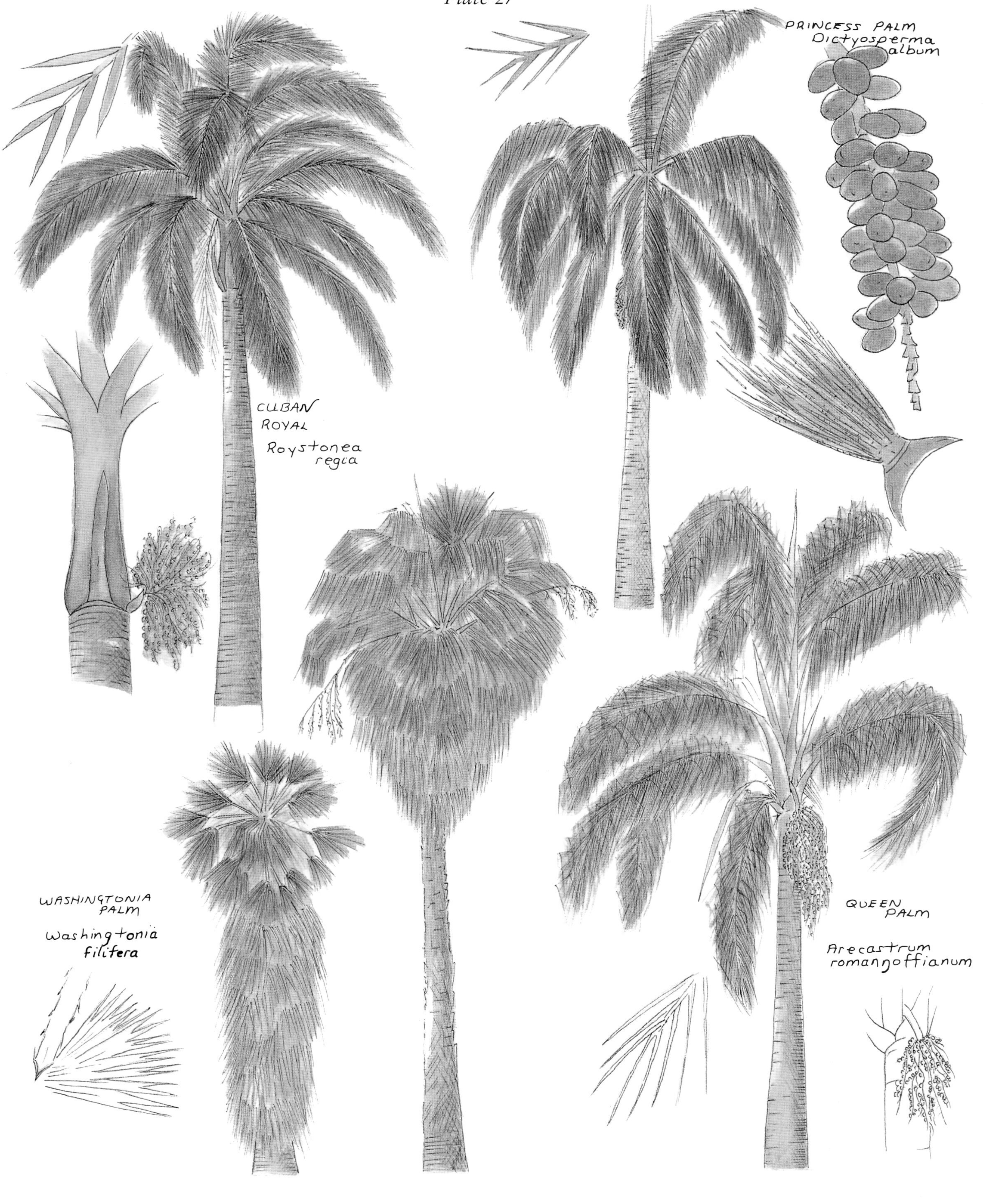
PRINCESS PALM
Dictyosperma album
CUBAN ROYAL
Roystonea regia
WASHINGTONIA PALM
Washingtonia filifera
QUEEN PALM
Arecastrum romanzoffianum

Chinese Fan Palm
Livistonia chinensis — Palmae

This palm is very commonly seen. Its single trunk comes in many sizes. The leaf petiole has spines to its base and the leaves are broad and cut halfway into narrow, one-ribbed segments, which are split again and the tips then hang on like a fringe. The fruits are bright turquoise with orange flesh.

European Fan Palm
Chamaerops humilis — Palmae

Origins in Mediterranean, South Europe and North Africa. Usually dwarf. This palm is quite rare in Bermuda. It suckers from the base, making a small trunk. The leaves are quite broad and flat, flowers are on short stems at the top of the plant. Fruit red-brown. Sub-tropical.

Fiji Fan Palm
Pritchardia pacifica — Palmae

From Fiji, Tonga and Samoa, this palm is not often seen in Bermuda. The leaves are stiff and grey-green. The flowers are in the crown and grow as long as the leaf stems, brown fibre at the base. Blue-black fruit.

Bermuda Palmetto
Sabal bermudana — Palmae

Endemic, palm tree up to 25 feet. Widespread but common in upland habitat. Locally common in peat marshes. Often featured in old Bermuda gardens. Identification point: curved leaves with yellow markings on leaf blades, blackish fruits. Other species of Palmetto found on the Carolina coast down to Florida.

Thatch Palm
Thrinax radiata — Palmae

From West Indies, Florida to Honduras. The leaves are chalky-green and paler on the underside. A fan palm with pinnate leaves, sliced and slightly folded from a distance. Known internationally as the West Indian Thatch Palm.

Behold, I have given you every herb-bearing seed, which is upon the face of all the earth, to you it shall be for meat.

EUROPEAN FAN PALM

Chamaerops humilis

FIJI FAN PALM
Pritchardia pacifica

CHINESE FAN PALM

Livistonia chinensis

BERMUDA PALMETTO
Sabal bermudana

THATCH PALM
Thrinax radiata

Yew

Podocarpus macrophyllus 'Maki' Podocarpaceae
From China, sometimes known as the Southern Yew. A hardy evergreen that is slowly spreading through wild areas of the Islands. Has dark green foliage that has a grey tinge to the back of the leaves. The birds love the fleshy oval fruit on female trees.

Japanese Pittosporum

Pittosporum undulatum Pittosporaceae
Seen planted as a hedgerow plant. Not common. Originating from Australia where oil is extracted from its fragrant flowers and the mature wood is used in the making of golf clubs.

Variegated Pittosporum

Pittosporum tobira variegata Pittosporaceae
From New Zealand cultivates with long, leathery leaves, narrow and glossy. Evergreen. Grows into a tree.

Victoria Box

Pittosporum tobira Pittosporaceae
From China and Japan, known internationally as 'Mock Orange'. A very tough local plant, shrub/small tree, evergreen. Thick, leathery, obovate, dark green leaves, arranged in dense whorls. Flowers very fragrant and arranged in clusters, creamy-white in colour. Seed pops open to reveal bright red shining fruits.

Oleander

Nerium oleander Apocynaceae
This well known shrub sometimes makes a considerable tree. As it is relatively new to the landscape one cannot tell the form it might take in the coming years. Its flowers come in various hues of pink and peach and can be seen from spring to the year's end. Some of the older Oleanders have grown into large trees.

Tamarisk

Tamarix gallica Tamaricaceae
A shrub, sometimes making a small tree. Arching feathery branches with reddish bark, tiny pink flowers in sprays on last year's growth. Originally from Europe and the Canary Islands. Planted by an early Governor along the north shore for protection from the cold winter winds. The most salt tolerant of any small tree in Bermuda.

Giant Privet

Ligustrum lucidum Oleaceae
A shrub that is very hardy, good for exposed areas. Dark green, glossy leaves and loose panicles of small white flowers.

Elaeagnus

Elaeagnus angustifolia Elaeagnaceae
Commonly called Russian Olive. A branching bush, up to 12 feet high. Brown stems with leathery, oval, shiny green leaves. Originally from Japan and China. Little silvery flowers.

Milk Bush Pencil Tree

Euphorbia tirucalli Euphorbiaceae
A shrub, sometimes making a tree; also known as the pencil plant, it seems to grow in any soil in any position. The milky sap causes a rash and is known to be poisonous. A good windbreak plant.

Pursuits, that to the heart
can bring
The pleasures of continual
Spring.
With summer's sweetest flowers.

American author

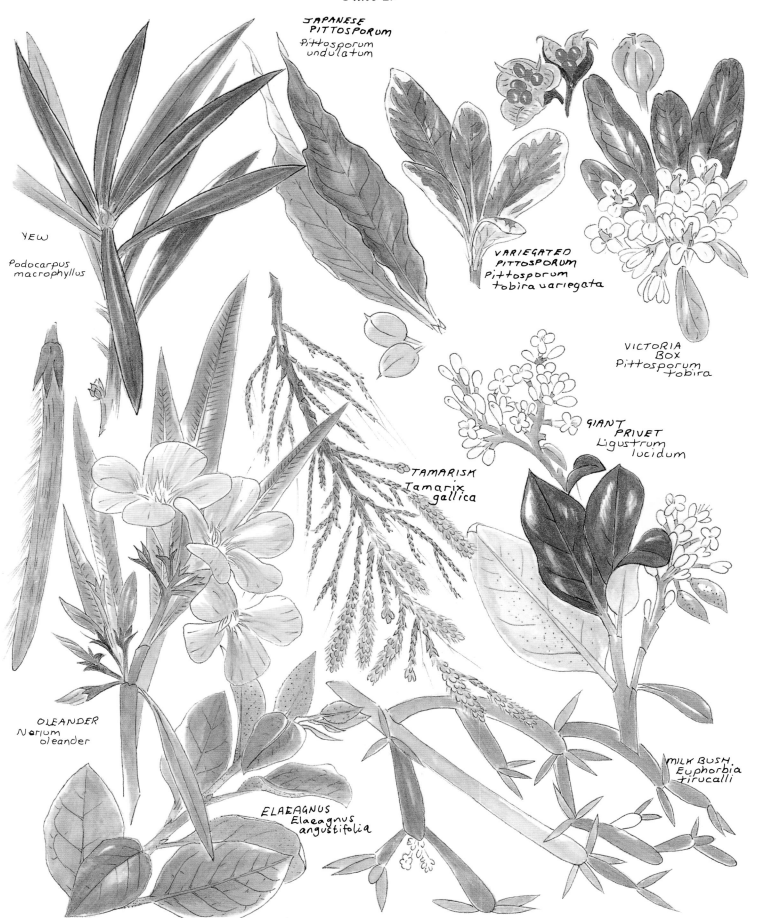

JAPANESE
PITTOSPORUM
*Pittosporum
undulatum*

YEW

*Podocarpus
macrophyllus*

VARIEGATED
PITTOSPORUM
*Pittosporum
tobira variegata*

VICTORIA
BOX
*Pittosporum
tobira*

GIANT
PRIVET
*Ligustrum
lucidum*

TAMARISK
*Tamarix
gallica*

OLEANDER
*Nerium
oleander*

MILK BUSH.
*Euphorbia
tirucalli*

ELAEAGNUS
*Elaeagnus
angustifolia*

Fiddlewood

Citharexylum spinosum   Verbenaceae
Origins: Tropical America to Argentina. Timber good. Locally a very popular tree, the woodlands are always ablaze with their golden-orange leaves in early summer followed by new growth and fountains of white flowers, very fragrant.

Allspice

Pimenta dioica   Myrtaceae
Originally from Jamaica to Central America. Bermuda has several small forests of Allspice. The tiny flowers are very fragrant, small and white. The berries are green, turning to reddish black. This same seed is actually the culinary 'Allspice'. The leaves are also very fragrant, pinnate and leathery.

Norfolk Island Pine

Araucaria excelsa (syn. *A. heterophylla)*   Araucariaceae
An evergreen tree originally from the South Pacific. A dramatic figure of note in the Bermuda landscape. Very stiff, formal branches running parallel to the ground. Should not be planted close to buildings as the shallow root system can easily erode in strong hurricane winds. Large seed like a small cannon.

Casuarina (Horsetail Tree)

Casuarina equisetifolia   Casuarinaceae
Known locally as the whistling pine, it was brought in on mass to Bermuda from Australia when the Cedar forests were devastated in the 1950s-60s. Grows up to 80 feet high. Its needle-like leaves bear tiny, fluffy red flowers and later many pine cones that are less than an inch in size and hang on for a few months. Burns well as firewood, thought by some to be one of the best firewoods in the world.

Italian Cypress

Cupressus sempervirens   Cupressaceae
This conical tree has quite short branches in a dense and narrow formation of up to 30 feet high. Its branches are stiff with dark green, scale-like leaves. Originally from Europe, west Asia and India.

To Flower and Plant and Tree,
The Garden is a cloistered refuge
from the battle of life.

NATURALIZED TREES
Plate 30

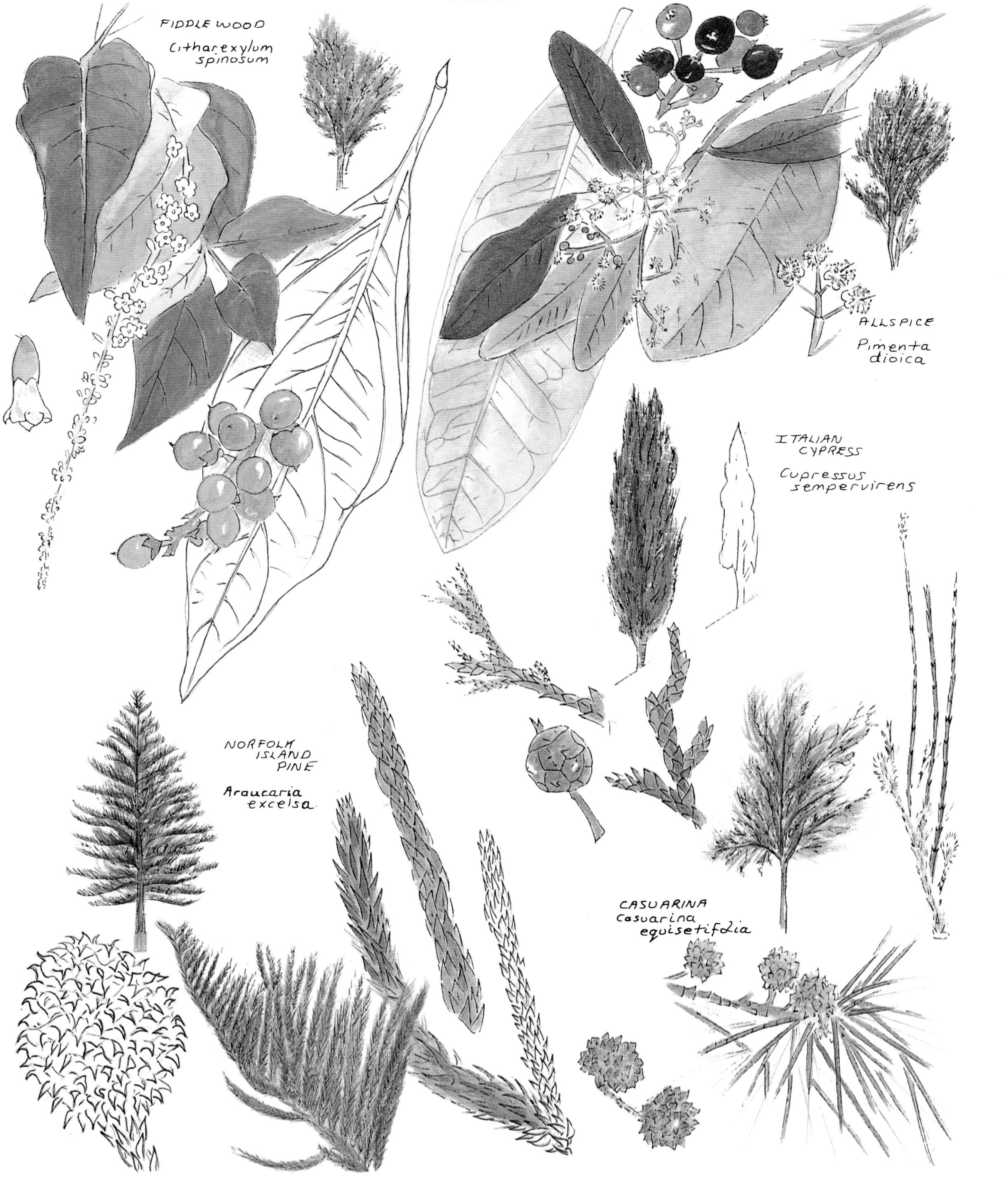
FIDDLEWOOD
Citharexylum spinosum
ALLSPICE
Pimenta dioica
ITALIAN CYPRESS
Cupressus sempervirens
NORFOLK ISLAND PINE
Araucaria excelsa
CASUARINA
Casuarina equisetifolia

Mahoe

Hibiscus tiliaceus   Malvaceae
A round-headed, medium-sized tree, rarely attaining more than 40 feet in height. Flowers open pale yellow 4 inches across in the morning, turning to hues of orange-red, later in the day falling to create a rich red carpet on the ground. Heart-shaped leaves are borne on long petioles, greyish-green in colour, and almost velvet to touch 6-8 inches long. Sometimes seen as a street tree, occasionally used for amenity planting.

Yellow Tecoma

Tecoma stans   Bignoniaceae
A shrub from tropical America. Flowers yellow. A popular ornamental garden plant.

Queen of Shrubs or Crape Myrtle

Lagerstroemia indica   Lythraceae
Originally from Japan, Korea and China. Known as the 'Crape Myrtle', a lovely flowering tree with elliptic leaves and clusters of frilled, pale purple flowers.

Carib Wood

Sabinia cardinalis   Leguminosae
A small tree with deep red flowers that often come into bloom before the leaves show. Pinnate, feathery leaves. Seed case twists as it matures showing a red fruit.

Edible Fig

Ficus carica   Moraceae
Originally from the Mediterranean area, often seen in old established gardens and hedgerows. Not a terrific flavour but will ripen. Leaves 5-7 lobed, pubescent. Fruit obovoid, tiny flowers, woody small tree.

Angels' Trumpets

Datura aurea (syn. *Brugmansia aurea*)   Solanaceae
A small tree up to 10 feet high. Flowers are cream-white, tubular and pendulous, The leaves also are pendulous and up to one foot long. Not many of these to be found on the Islands. Mostly seen in established gardens.

Yellow Oleander or Lucky Nut

Thevetia peruviana   Apocynaceae
Originally from tropical America. Evergreen small tree or shrub with shining green leaves, funnel-shaped flowers in yellow and orange, forming fruits as large as the flowers and pouch like. Poisonous.

Everlasting Senna

Senna floribunda (syn. *Cassia floribunda*)   Leguminosae
Originally from Brazil, this is a small tree with bright yellow flowers that hold from winter until spring. It is in the Leguminosae family and like others in its family adds a delightful colour to the Bermuda landscape.

Dombeya

Dombeya wallichii   Sterculiaceae
Found first in east Africa and Madagascar, evergreen yet gets very windblown in Bermuda. Largish lobed leaves, quite hairy beneath. Lovely pink flowers growing densely in hanging heads.

In days when daisies deck
the sod
And blackbirds whistle clear,
Wi' honest joy our hearts
will bound
To greet the coming year!

Burns

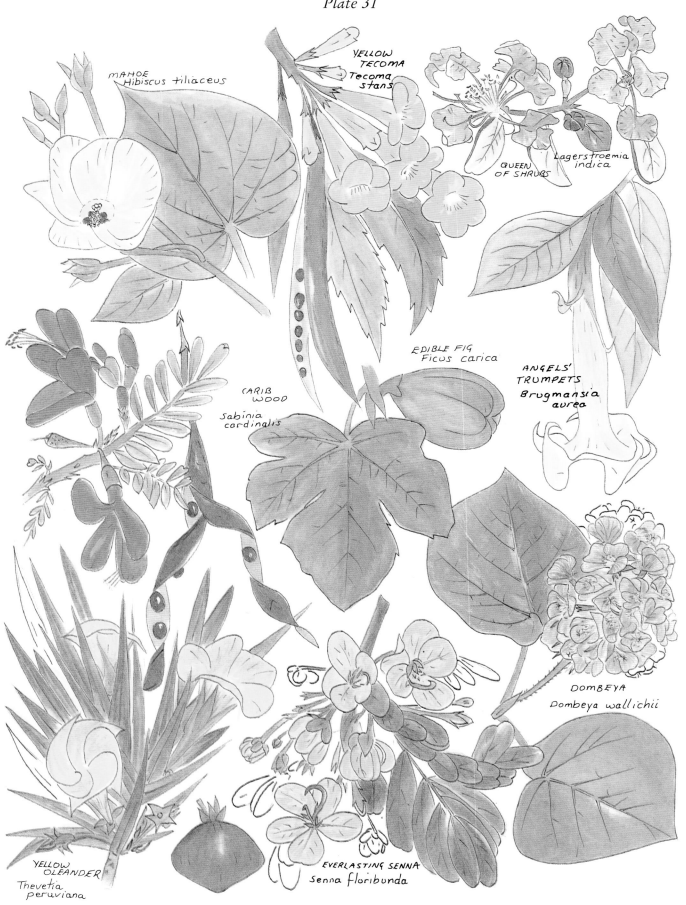

MAHOE
Hibiscus tiliaceus

YELLOW
TECOMA
Tecoma
stans

QUEEN
OF SHRUBS

Lagerstroemia
indica

EDIBLE FIG
Ficus carica

ANGELS'
TRUMPETS
Brugmansia
aurea

CARIB
WOOD
Sabinia
cardinalis

DOMBEYA
Dombeya wallichii

YELLOW
OLEANDER
Thevetia
peruviana

EVERLASTING SENNA
Senna floribunda

Fiddle Leaf Fig

Ficus lyrata   Moraceae

Originally from tropical West Africa, has very large leathery leaves (in the shape of a fiddle). Fruits quite large, at times the size of a chicken's egg, with concave markings. Yellow-green veins on a woody stem. Not commonly seen but a good specimen in the Botanical Gardens.

Peepul Tree or Sacred Fig

Ficus religiosa   Moraceae

Originally from India, a wonderful specimen seen in the Botanical Gardens and Torwood in Somerset. History has said that it was under this tree in the Far East that Buddha received enlightenment. Blue-green leaves, heart-shaped with a tail-like tip. Purple fruit, quite small. Grows up to 100 feet.

Weeping Fig

Ficus benjamina   Moraceae

Originally from India, this tree has a habit of forming aerial roots. Its pendulous, shining, dark green leaves are long-ovate in shape; small fruits, quite red when ripe. It is similar to the Indian Laurel tree but its habit is far more weeping in appearance or form

Ban Yan Tree

Ficus benghalensis   Moraceae

Orginally from India and Ceylon. One of the few Ficus species that takes up large areas. It produces aerial roots that secure themselves to the ground, developing a network of secondary trunks. It has large leaves, and seeds of deep orange which are round. There is a lovely example in the Botanical Gardens. It can spread for hundreds of feet.

Australian Ban Yan

Ficus macrophylla   Moraceae

Used as a street shade tree in Sydney, Australia. There is a very good specimen in the Botanical Gardens.

Indian Laurel

Ficus retusa   Moraceae

Sometimes called the Chinese Ban Yan, perhaps because it originates from that side of the world. Small leathery leaves are quite waxy. A good shade tree (but also a very messy seed fall). It anchors itself to the ground by roots off its branches which almost hold up the trunk. Easily seeds itself anywhere. Could prove a pest on the islands.

Indian Rubber Tree

Ficus elastica   Moraceae

Originally from India, it is a commonly known house plant, although in Bermuda it grows into a huge tree. It has broad, shiny, dark green leaves and one should be careful where one plants this tree as aggressive roots can easily crack local water tanks and house foundations. Its sap is a strong white latex fluid; seeds are quite small.

To a Butterfly

I've watched you now a full
half hour,
Self-poised upon that
yellow flower,
And, little butterfly indeed
I know not if you sleep or feed
How motionless and then
What joy awaits you, when
the breeze
Hath found you out among
the trees
And calls you forth again.

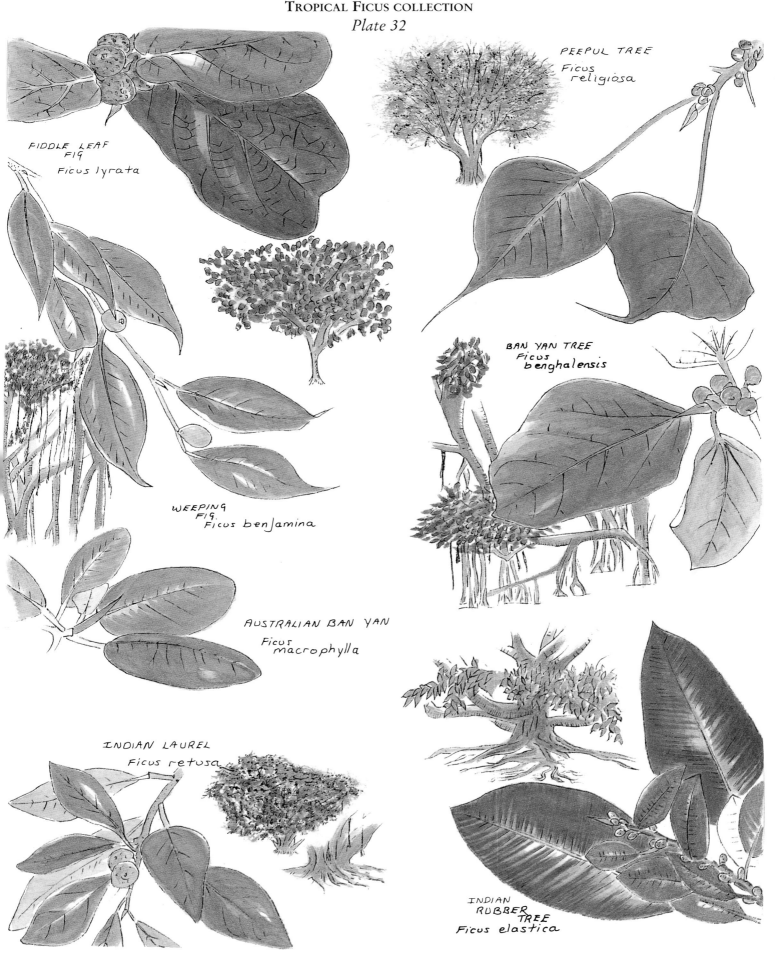

PEEPUL TREE
Ficus religiósa

FIDDLE LEAF FIG
Ficus lyrata

BAN YAN TREE
Ficus benghalensis

WEEPING FIG.
Ficus benjamina

AUSTRALIAN BAN YAN
Ficus macrophylla

INDIAN LAUREL
Ficus retusa

INDIAN RUBBER TREE
Ficus elastica

33 Smaller tropical trees

Octopus Tree (Australian Ivy Palm or Umbrella Tree)
Schefflera actinophylla   Araliaceae
First found in Queensland, Java and New Guinea, also known
as the Umbrella Tree. Makes quite a tall tree in Bermuda. Its
rosette of leaves form on woody branches (palmately
compound leaves, soft and leathery). Flowers in straight spikes
with wine coloured, thick petals which, when mature, form
into purple fruits.

Loquat (Japanese)
Eriobotrya japonica   Rosaceae
From China, this is a very popular local small tree. Fruits
enjoyed by all in preserves and pies. Also very decorative dark
green foliage. Leaves slightly toothed – underside quite hairy,
woolly substance which carries into the flowers of rust and
ruffled cream petals, very fragrant. Fruits small, orange and
pear shape. Seeds within brown and shiny.

Bottle Brush
Callistemon citrinus   Myrtaceae
Bright red flowers on spikes that resemble a bottle brush.
Originally from Australia. Found growing in many gardens, it
appears to be quite hardy, growing up to approximately 25 feet
high.

White Cordia
Cordia dentata   Boraginaceae
From tropical America, not often seen in Bermuda but a lovely
small tree. Tiny pale yellow flowers in clusters with dark green
leaves with toothed margins. Internationally known as
'Jaekwood'.

Scarlet Cordia
Cordia sebestena   Boraginaceae
Originally found in the West Indies and Florida areas. A small
tree often used as a street tree, to 25 feet high. Dark green, oval
leaves in clusters on branch ends. Flowers bright orange-red,
ruffled look to petals. Fruit white, slightly conical, fleshy, said
to be edible.

Varnish Tree
Koelreuteria paniculata   Sapindaceae
Came from Fiji, known as the Chinese Rain Tree or Shrimp
Tree. Flat topped from a distance and of medium size. Leaflets
narrow, ovate and rich green. Small yellow flowers with pink-
salmon seed cases which are rather papery to the touch.
Widely cultivated in Central Europe as a street tree.

Frangipani (White and Pink)
Plumeria alba and P. rubra   Apocynaceae
From Mexico, known as the 'Temple Tree' of India. Leaves
pinnate and wedge shaped. Flowers very fragrant white, with a
yellow throat in the funnel form dimension. Deciduous and
looks like a stilt construction in wintertime. Pink flowers of *P.
rubra* offered in Buddhist temples.

Jerusalem Thorn
Parkinsonia aculeata   Leguminosae
Originally from tropical America to Cape Verde Island. A
small, spiny, ornamental tree, very long arching stems with
narrow bi-pinnate foliage. Small, yellow flowers with fruits
forming into a pod.

I have a garden of my own
Shining with flowers of
every hue,
I loved it dearly while alone
But I shall love it more
with you.

Thomas More 1835

Smaller tropical trees

Plate 33

BOTTLE BRUSH
Callistemon citrinus
OCTOPUS TREE
Schefflera actinophylla
LOQUAT
Eriobotrya japonica
WHITE CORDIA
Cordia dentata
JERUSALEM THORN
Parkinsonia aculeata
SCARLET CORDIA
Cordia sebestena
FRANGIPANI
Plumeria alba
VARNISH TREE
Koelreuteria paniculata
Plumeria rubra

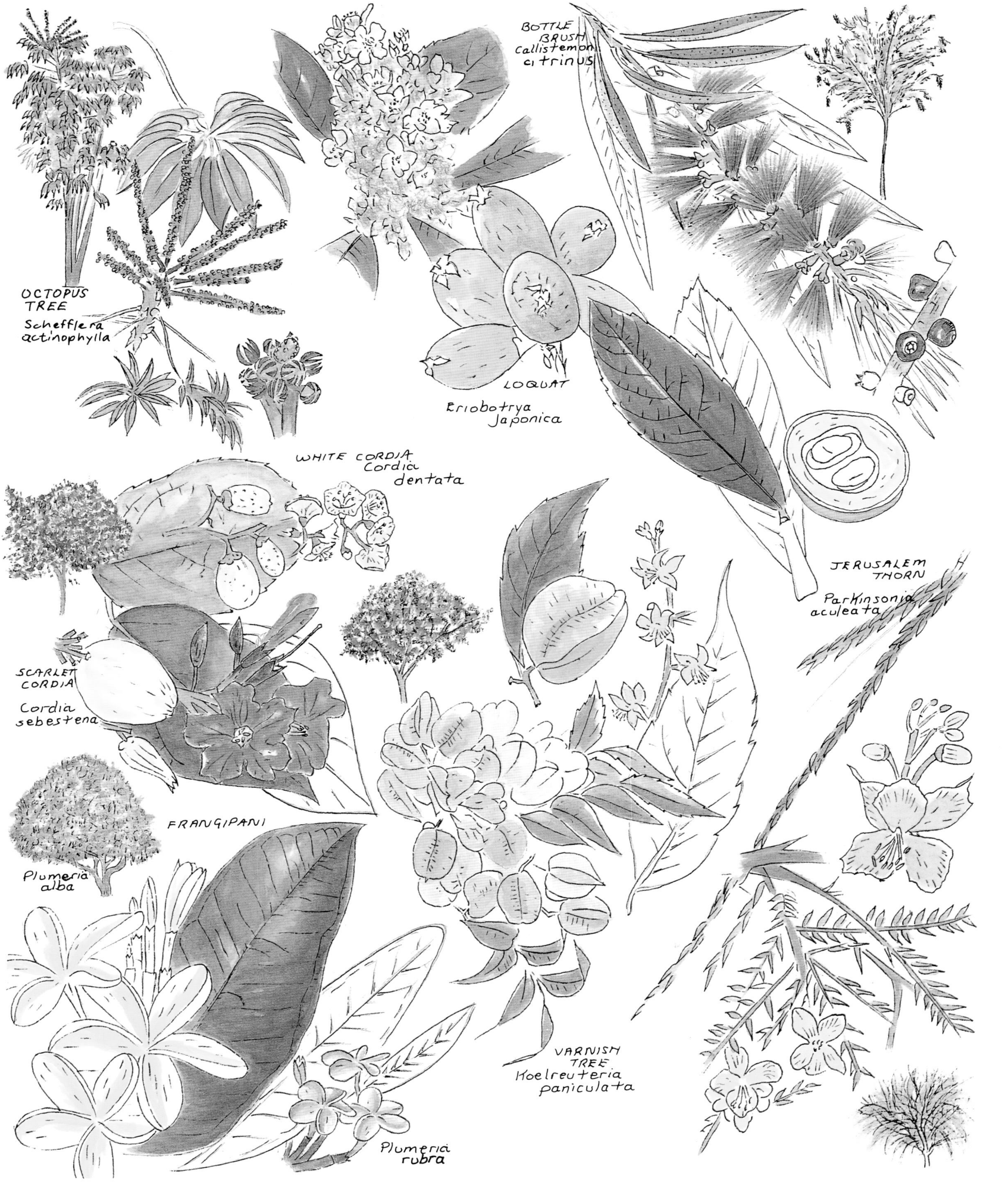

Red River Gum Tree
Eucalyptus camaldulensis Myrtaceae
Originally from Western Australia, a medium size tree with willowy, brown stems and blue-grey leaves, quite leathery and aromatic. Many flowers in umbels, bright red and stamens at base of calyx in a ring formation.

Giant Flowered Magnolia
Magnolia grandiflora Magnoliaceae
Native of the southern states, known as the Southern Magnolia. Evergreen, with thick green, large, ovate, oblong leaves with underside quite rusty and suede-like to the touch. Very large, cup-shaped cream flowers, fragrant. Brown cone-like fruit that houses red seeds in the autumn season. A popular plant, grown in large gardens.

Kumani
Calophyllum inophyllum Guttiferaceae
Very fleshy ovate leaves, large, round seed pods. Very hardy, planted frequently for ornamental reasons, sometimes for protection from the high winds.

White Cedar or Trumpet Tree
Tabebuia pallida Bignoniaceae
Originally from the West Indies and Central North America, also known as the Cuban Pink Trumpet Tree. The pink flowers are very showy, in dense clusters. A tinge of pale yellow in the throat of the flower. The fruit forms a long pod. At times locally it is partly deciduous and flowers may appear before leaves, but often at the same time.

Mahogany Tree
Swietenia mahogani Meliaceae
Found in old established gardens, an evergreen tree that often loses its leaves in the winter due to the winter storms. Small white flowers, large brown seed pods. The wood is much sought after for furniture making.

Away before me to sweet beds of flowers,
Love thoughts lie rich when canopied with bowers.

Shakespeare

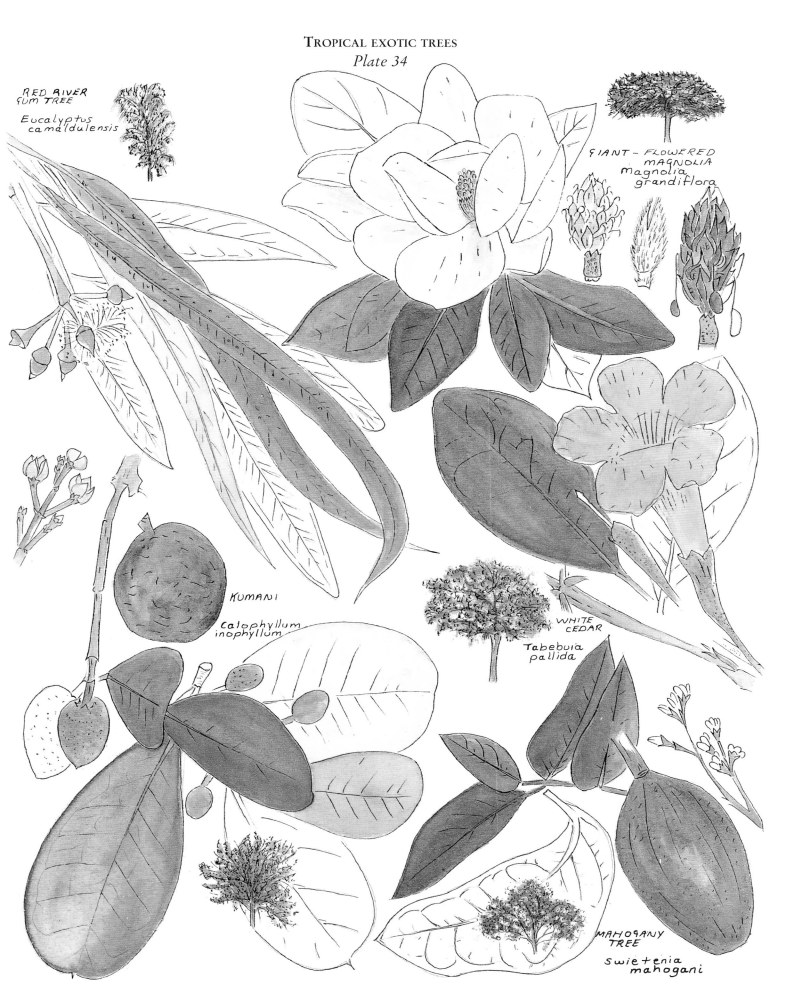

RED RIVER
GUM TREE

*Eucalyptus
camaldulensis*

GIANT-FLOWERED
MAGNOLIA
*Magnolia
grandiflora*

KUMANI

*Calophyllum
inophyllum*

WHITE
CEDAR

*Tabebuia
pallida*

MAHOGANY
TREE

*Swietenia
mahogani*

Pink Shower

Cassia javanica — Leguminosae

Found originally in Indonesia, known sometimes as the Apple Blossom Shower. Low and spreading in form with layers of pinnate leaves almost parallel to the ground. Petals pink with bright yellow stamens.

Pride of India or China Berry

Melia azedarach — Meliaceae

Originally from India and China, deciduous in Bermuda. Bi-pinnate foliage with feathery, toothed leaves. Clusters of pale lilac flowers with darker purple markings, fruits bright yellow – poisonous – usually seen when tree is leafless. The wood is said to be good for furniture making.

Golden Shower

Cassia fistula — Leguminosae

From India and Sri Lanka, a lovely tree with pinnate leaves in pairs. Bright yellow, fragrant flowers in drooping racemes – another tree that looks like the sun has arrived on earth when in full flower. Partly deciduous.

West Indian Almond

Terminalia catappa — Combretaceae

Originally found in the East Indies, known internationally as the Tropical Almond. Quite a small tree with wide spreading branches, large obovate leathery leaves, which turn red before they fall. Flowers tiny, white-green on spikes followed by green fruits with oil-bearing seeds which are edible but do not mature well here.

African Tulip Tree

Spathodea campanulata — Bignoniaceae

A West African forest tree with long pinnate leaves, the scarlet flowers appear early in the summer, also in the autumn. They are enclosed in a brown suede sheath. The tree was planted extensively to commemorate the coronation of King George VI. The seed case has hundreds of papery seeds within.

If you want to be happy all your life – make a garden.

PINK
SHOWER
Cassia
Javanica

PRIDE OF
INDIA
Melia
azedarach

GOLDEN
SHOWER
Cassia
fistula

WEST
INDIAN
ALMOND
Terminalia
catappa

AFRICAN TULIP TREE
Spathodea
campanulata

Surinam Cherry

Eugenia uniflora   Myrtaceae

Introduced to Bermuda in the 1800s. Originally from Brazil and Guyana, a small tree, dense semi-evergreen, fruiting, used locally for hedging. Reaches up to 20 feet high. Small ovate leaves and fragrant flowers producing a delicious red edible fruit that has a slightly spicy flavour. Used locally to make jams and other culinary delights. Taking over as a secondary forest due to birds dropping seed islandwide after feeding frenzies. Can become very invasive. Cherry season is popular with locals and tourists. Normally fruits twice a year.

Calabash Tree

Crescentia cujete   Bignoniaceae

Originally from the tropical Americas, the Calabash grows up to 25 feet with striking erect branches on which the 'cannon-ball-like' fruit form on the bark. The flowers are green with maroon markings. The fruits form a hard shell which has many uses locally including salad bowls, bird boxes and bailers. This tree is deciduous and loses its leaves in the winter months. The first mention of the Calabash in Bermuda was via the poet Tom Moon who wrote his famous verse while sitting under the Old Calabash Tree in Walsingham Jungle. It was thought to have been devastated by the 1987 storm though now happily it has sent out new growth.

Sausage Tree

Kigelia africana   Bignoniaceae

A rarely seen tree, dramatically large and unusual plant with enormous deep red flowers and even more enormous hanging seed that resembles a sausage hanging on a stem.

Olive

Olea europea   Oleaceae

First found in the Mediterranean, a small grey-green tree that looks silvery from a distance. Leaves narrow and quite leathery, flowers cream and fragrant. Oblong fruits appear green and turn black when ripe. Used in its homeland to make olive oil for international usage. With maturity and old age this tree becomes gnarled and an interesting landscape tree. It is thought the Spanish first planted the Olive Tree in Bermuda in the sixteenth century when they landed on the Island. Bermuda's climate is not conducive to good fruit.

It is impossible for any man to have plants to prosper, unless he love them.

John Rea 1665

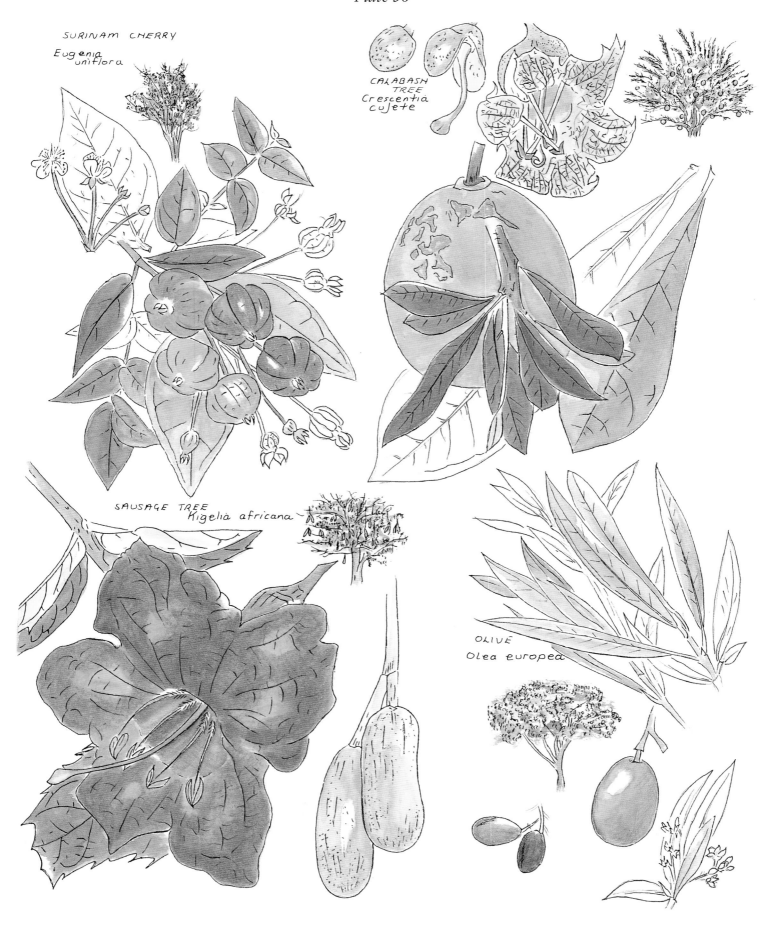

SURINAM CHERRY
Eugenia uniflora

CALABASH TREE
Crescentia cujete

SAUSAGE TREE
Kigelia africana

OLIVE
Olea europea

Sword Tree or Coral Tree

Erythrina caffra   Leguminosae

From Cape Province, Natal. Spiked, bright red flowers. Seed case has black exterior with bright red seeds. Deciduous tree, flowers often before leaves. Leaves spade shaped with flowers being tubular.

Flame Tree

Brachychiton acerifolius   Sterculiaceae

A rarely seen tree, a few specimens in private gardens. One particularly good specimen is next to the library in the Botanical Gardens.

Bauhinia

Bauhinia acuminata   Leguminosae

Known as the Orchid or Butterfly Tree, orginally from India and China. Semi-deciduous tree with thin butterfly-like leaves of a dullish green colour. Lovely orchid-like flowers in white or rose-carmine with purple markings. Seed flat, a pea-like formation.

Silk Oak

Grevillea robusta   Proteaceae

Found originally in Queensland and New South Wales, Australia, a fair sized tree in Bermuda. Silvery-green fern-like leaves. Flowers gold-orange, fruits brown, lobed with a tail formation. This is an evergreen tree.

Tree Hibiscus

Thespesia populnea   Malvaceae

From Asia and Polynesia, a multi-branched tree with large, cordate, hairy leaves. Flowers lemon and deep orange-red, changing to darker shades from day to night. Sometimes called Manhoe.

Hedgerows all alive,
With birds and gnats and large
white butterflies
Which look as if the May
Flower had caught life
And palpitated forth upon
the wind.

E.B. Browning

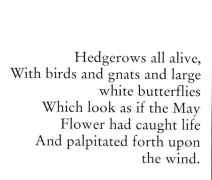

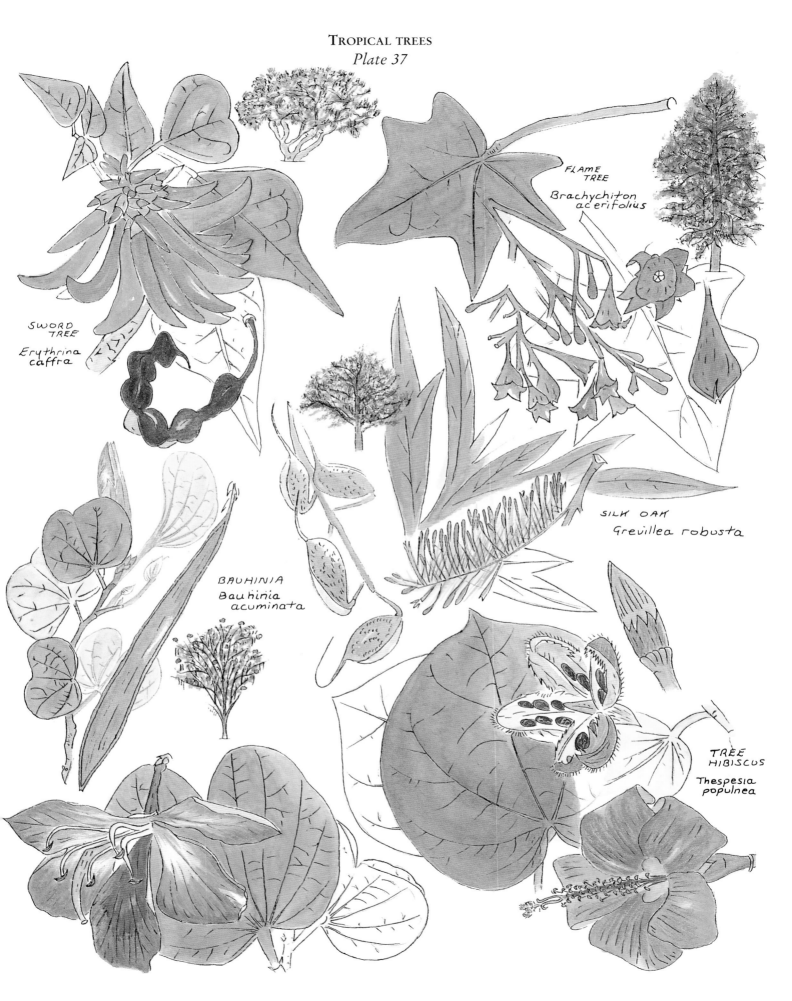

FLAME
TREE
Brachychiton
acerifolius

SWORD
TREE
Erythrina
caffra

SILK OAK
Grevillea robusta

BAUHINIA
Bauhinia
acuminata

TREE
HIBISCUS

Thespesia
populnea

Black Ebony
Albizia lebbeck — Leguminosae

Large trees planted frequently. As they are deciduous they can be messy but its beautiful, fragrant, puff-ball flowers seem to outweigh the extra sweeping up in the wintertime. Long beige pods then form and can be seen hanging on even after the leaves drop. Leaves are feather-like, 1 inch across. This makes a lovely summer shade tree.

Yellow Poinciana
Peltophorum pterocarpum — Leguminosae

Sometimes called Barbados Pride. A deciduous shrub with similar flowers to the Royal Poinciana although yellow and much smaller. Blooms in the summertime.

Royal Poinciana
Delonix regia — Leguminosae

Originally from tropical Africa, Madagascar and India. An extremely popular tree although it has no foliage for a major part of the year. But when the tiny feathery leaves appear in the spring it is well worth the wait. The bright red flowers have the most dramatic effect on the landscape of any plant. The large black seed pods often remain on the tree for many months.

Tamarind
Tamarindus indica — Leguminosae

The 'Tamarind Tree', as it is known, comes originally from tropical Africa. You will find a lovely specimen in the National Trust headquarters' garden. Its leaves are feathery and pinnate and it has small flowers which are delicate greens with deep red tiny markings. Seed pods commonly seen.

Jacaranda
Jacaranda mimosifolia — Bignoniaceae

Originally from Brazil, a tree that is a wonder on the Bermudan landscape. Although not many have been planted the erect clusters of lilac-blue flowers with their tubular shape add a brightness to the landscape never to be forgotten. The seed is rounded and quite flat.

We shape our dwellings.
And afterwards our dwellings
shape us.

Sir Winston Churchill

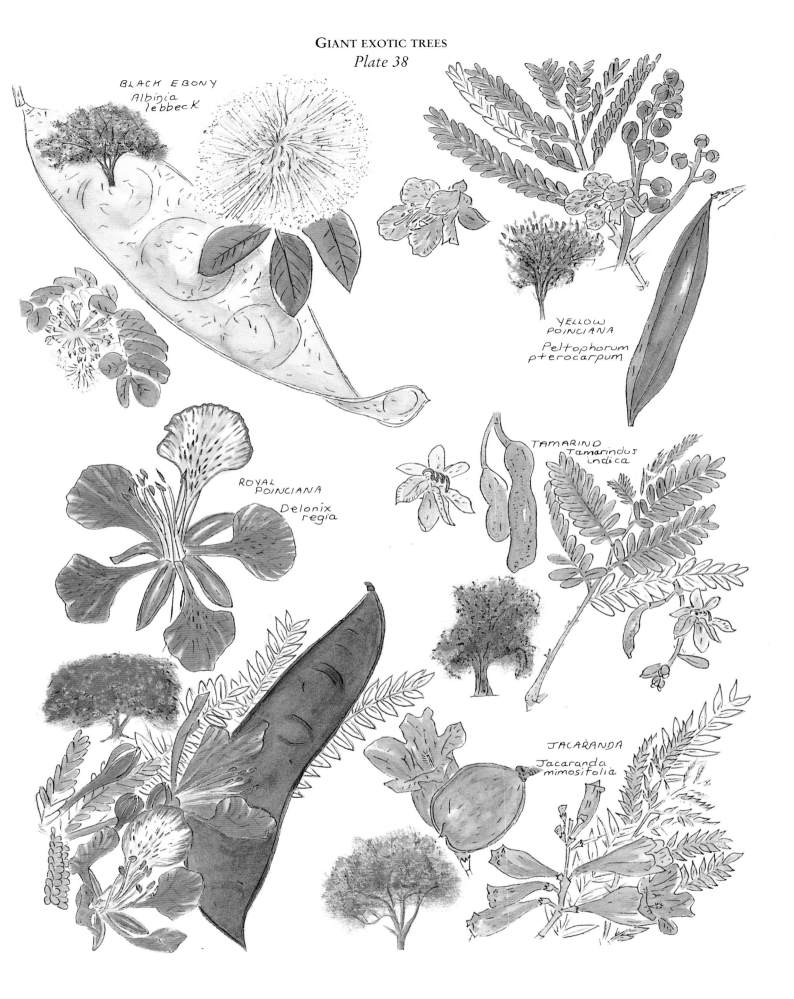

BLACK EBONY
Albinia lebbeck

YELLOW POINCIANA
Peltophorum pterocarpum

ROYAL POINCIANA
Delonix regia

TAMARIND
Tamarindus indica

JACARANDA
Jacaranda mimosifolia

Fern Asparagus

Asparagus sectaceus   Liliaceae

It is seen frequently in hedgerows. Originating from South Africa. Grown elsewhere for use by florists in buttonholes etc.

Asparagus Fern

Asparagus densiflorus   Liliaceae

One of the most commonly seen plants around the Island, inhabiting both coastal and upland areas, often under Casuarinas. Spreads by underground tubers which form new plants when detached. Produces long, arching stems covered in short, sharp light green leaflets. Flowers white 1/4 inch across in clusters followed by red seeds or berries. A good ground cover plant for difficult sloping sites or very shady areas.

Holly Fern

Cyrtomium falcatum   Dryopteridaceae

Perhaps the toughest of all the true ferns found in Bermuda, a naturalized introduction spreading rapidly in upland habitats throughout the Islands. Often seen growing out of semi-shaded, limestone rocky outcrops only short distances from the sea (Spittal Pond). Its common name refers to its 'holly-shaped' leaves which distinguish it from any other fern. Inland it may be found in sheltered spots at the entrance of caves. In Bermuda it rarely grows above 12 inches high.

Bermuda Shield Fern

Dryopteris bermudiana   Aspleniaceae

Once thought to have been widespread in the Walsingham Castle Harbour rocky outcrops and sinks. Now thought to be on the verge of extinction despite efforts to raise spores from plants of this species.

Long Leaf Asparagus Fern

Asparagus officinalis   Liliaceae

A rampant, potentially invasive, vine differing from *A. sprengerii* in having tough lanceolate leaves up to 2 inches long. White not commonly seen around the Island, where it has established it is very difficult to eradicate. Its tough stems are covered in sharp hook-like spines which cling and tear at passers-by with considerable venom.

Bracken

Pteridium aquilinum var. *pseudo-caudatum*   Pteridaceae

Found growing mainly in Paget and Devonshire Marshes. Grows up to 3 feet high. Tends to die back in the wintertime.

Long-Leaved Brake

Pteris longifolia   Pteridaceae

Seen islandwide along walls and gardens. Naturalized. Native of Florida and tropical America. Established in Bermuda in 1883.

Sword Fern

Nephrolepis exaltata   Davalliaceae

Native, widespread and fairly common in both upland and peat marsh habitats. It also grows in axils of palm leaves and hollows of trees.

Ten-Day Fern

Polystichum adiantiforme   Polypodiaceae

Found occasionally in marshland and shaded rock areas, surviving only in Devonshire Marsh.

Creeping Fern

Phymatosorus scolopendria   Polypodiaceae

A naturalized introduction. Rapidly invading and spreading, especially in the Walsingham area.

Plume Polypody

Polypodium plumula   Polypodiaceae

Native found in Walsingham Cave Jungle area, originally from the West Indies. Numerous leaves pinnate, narrow lanceolate.

Cut-Leaved Brake

Anopteris hexagona   Polypodiaceae

Found in a few cave habitats in Harrington Sound and Castle Harbour. Native to the West Indies.

Large Marsh Shield Fern

Dryopteris normalis   Polypodiaceae

Seen frequently in the larger marsh areas. Native to Florida and the West Indies.

Maidenair Fern

Adiantum bellum   Adiantaceae

Endemic. Widespread and fairly common in localized areas, such as shaded rock faces, road cuts, etc. within the Islands.

Long Spleenwort

Asplenium heterochroum   Aspleniaceae

Quite rare, occasionally found in old walls in nature reserves. Must not be picked from the wild.

Toothed Spleenwort

Asplenium dentatum   Aspleniaceae

Native. Widespread, uncommon but rare and localized in caves and shaded rock faces in upland sites. Mostly in Walsingham cave district.

Bermuda Cave Fern

Ctenitis sloanei   Aspleniaceae

Extremely rare and now confined and surviving in two sites only. Castle Harbour area.

Virginia Chain Fern

Woodwardia virginica   Polypodiaceae

Uncommon to rare, and localized in Devonshire and Paget Marshes.

Governor Laffan's Fern

Diplazium laffanianum   Woodsiaceae

Endemic. Formerly uncommon in Walsingham Cave district but extinct in the wild since 1905. Cultivated specimens survive in the Botanical Gardens.

Cinnamon Fern

Osmunda cinnamomea   Osmundaceae

Native of eastern North America to Mexico. Large rootstock, widely creeping. Leaves pinnate linear-lanceolate, into oblong obtuse segments. The spores are discharged when green, leaving cinnamon-coloured spikes amidst the dense green foliage.

Royal Fern

Osmunda regalis   Osmundaceae

Common in the larger marshland areas. Native also of North America, Europe and Asia.

Giant Leather Fern

Acrostichum danaeifolium (syn. *Acrostichum excelsum*)
                                        Pteridaceae

Found in most Bermuda marshlands, native of Florida and the West Indies. Sometimes reaches up to 8 feet high. Root base solitary, fairly woody, leaf blades strong and leathery, with rust-suede effect. Dense spores on the back of leaves. A large stand at the entrance to Paget Marsh.

Such pritie things would
soon be gon
If we should not them so
remembre –

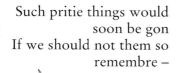

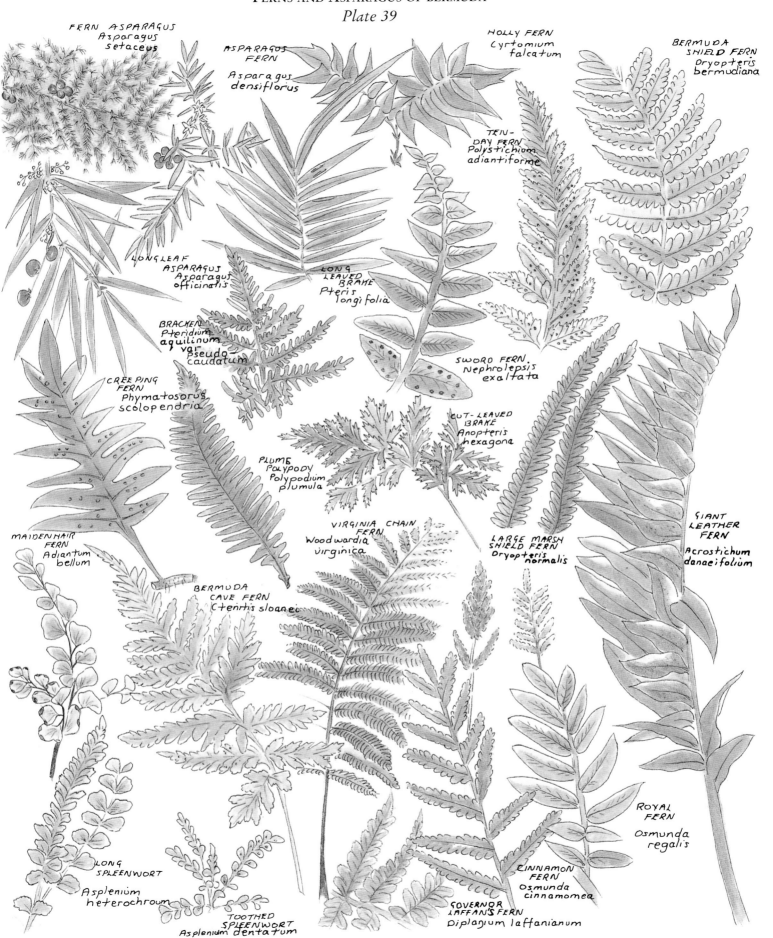

FERN ASPARAGUS
Asparagus
setaceus

ASPARAGUS
FERN

Asparagus
densiflorus

HOLLY FERN
Cyrtomium
falcatum

BERMUDA
SHIELD FERN
Dryopteris
bermudiana

TEN-
DAY FERN
Polystichium
adiantiforme

LONGLEAF
ASPARAGUS
Asparagus
officinalis

LONG
LEAVED
BRAKE
Pteris
longifolia

BRACKEN
Pteridium
aquilinum
var
pseudo-
caudatum

SWORD FERN
Nephrolepsis
exaltata

CREEPING
FERN
Phymatosorus
scolopendria

CUT-LEAVED
BRAKE
Anopteris
hexagona

PLUME
POLYPODY
Polypodium
plumula

GIANT
LEATHER
FERN

Acrostichum
danaeifolium

VIRGINIA CHAIN
FERN
Woodwardia
virginica

LARGE MARSH
SHIELD FERN
Dryopteris
normalis

MAIDENHAIR
FERN
Adiantum
bellum

BERMUDA
CAVE FERN
Ctenitis sloanei

ROYAL
FERN

Osmunda
regalis

LONG
SPLEENWORT

Asplenium
heterochroum

CINNAMON
FERN
Osmunda
cinnamomea

TOOTHED
SPLEENWORT
Asplenium dentatum

GOVERNOR
LAFFAN'S FERN
Diplazium laffanianum

Fox Tail Grass

Chaetochloe verticillata   Gramineae

Seen on most open cultivated ground, flowers through much of the year. Has a tufted and hairy appearance. There are other species of Fox Tail grasses, they add a lovely dimension to the local vegetation.

Rye Grass

Elymus virginicus   Gramineae

Introduced into Bermuda from North America, it is quite commonly used with Bermuda grass and crab grass to create a good lawn turf. If allowed to run wild it grows up to 2 feet high and flowers and seeds with great profusion.

Cane Grass

Panicum dichotomiflorum   Gramineae

Seen frequently along roadsides and in damp areas. Can grow quite tall, possibly over 4 feet. Naturalized in eastern USA. Flowers in summer and autumn.

Common Quaking Grass

Briza media   Gramineae

Native of Europe. Naturalized in Jamaica, also introduced into USA. Often found in fields, grassland and on roadside banks. Flowers in April. Narrow leaves, flower/seed heads grow on ends of spikelets. *Maxima* – a larger form of quaking grass.

Lesser Quaking Grass

Briza minor   Gramineae

A larger and taller version of *Briza media*, with broader flower heads.

Oats

Avena sativa   Gramineae

Possibly the new name is *Avena futula* as for the common wild oat. Occasionally seen along roadsides and waste ground, up to 12 inches long.

Wire Grass

Eleusine indica   Gramineae

Commonly seen islandwide. Also abundant over much of North America. Naturalized from the old world warmer regions. Seems to flower for most of the year.

Burr Grass

Cenchrus tribuloides   Gramineae

Found mostly in sand dunes. Seed head a very spiky burr head, that can give a very painful sting if one brushes against it. Flowers spring to autumn. It is thought the buds came to Bermuda on ocean currents.

Bull Grass

Sporobolus berteroanus   Gramineae

Slender and wiry plant quite commonly seen, native to southern USA and Bahamas. Flowers in summer and autumn.

Switch Grass

Panicum virgatum   Gramineae

Native of eastern North America and Cuba. Seeds came to Bermuda possibly by birds or wind. Flowers late summer, erect from stout root stock, tall leaf blades.

Salt Grass

Spartina patens   Gramineae

Found along rocky, sandy coastline. Native. Flowers in summer.

Annual Meadow Grass

Poa annua   Gramineae

Abundant in established lawns. Leaves broad, March/May flower spikes appear.

Beard Grass

Polypogon fugax   Gramineae

Found occasionally along hedgerows and waste places. Flowers in the summer.

Bermuda Grass

Cynodon dactylon   Gramineae

Common Bermuda grass used in most local lawns, a very fine texture that is usually mixed with other grasses.

West Indian Grass

Eustachys petraea (syn. *Chloris petraea*)   Gramineae

Found occasionally colonizing coastal hedgerows. Seed heads are very attractive and may be used in flower arrangements.

Baldwins Cyperus

Cyperus globulosus   Cyperaceae

Found along borders of marshes, sandy fields, hillsides and occasionally in gardens.

Wild Oat

Avena sativa (sub sp. *fatula*)   Gramineae

A grass from the old world now naturalized in the western USA. Tall, with nodding smooth sheaths that house the flower parts, tiny ring of brown hairs at the base.

Crab Grass

Stenotaphrum secundatum   Gramineae

Found growing in many tropical areas of the world. It is the predominant lawn grass in Bermuda. Very hardy, fairly salt tolerant, quickly spreading, creeping roots form a closely woven mat or turf. Easily propagated by division of rooting rhizomes.

Seashore Rush Grass

Sporobolus virginicus   Gramineae

Commonly found along much of the coastline, in dense spiky tussocks of tufted grass. Helps in the stabilization of dune areas.

Sheathed Paspalum

Paspalum vaginatum   Gramineae

Dominant vegetation of salt-marsh. Found along areas of Bermuda's coastline, particularly in Spittal Pond where it has helped the stabilization of the inland dune areas (it is often used in tropical areas to stabilize dunes).

Slender Paspalum

Paspalum caespitosum   Gramineae

Native. Tufted leaves devoid of hairs, very narrow spikelets in pairs. Found flowering in summer and autumn.

Chapman's Paspalum

Paspalum chapmani   Gramineae

Found islandwide, fairly abundant along arable and cultivated land, flowering summer and autumn.

Joint Grass

Paspalum distichum   Gramineae

Frequently seen in marshland and wastelands. Native.

The pleached bower
where honeysuckles
ripened by the sun,
Forbid the sun to enter.

Shakespeare

112

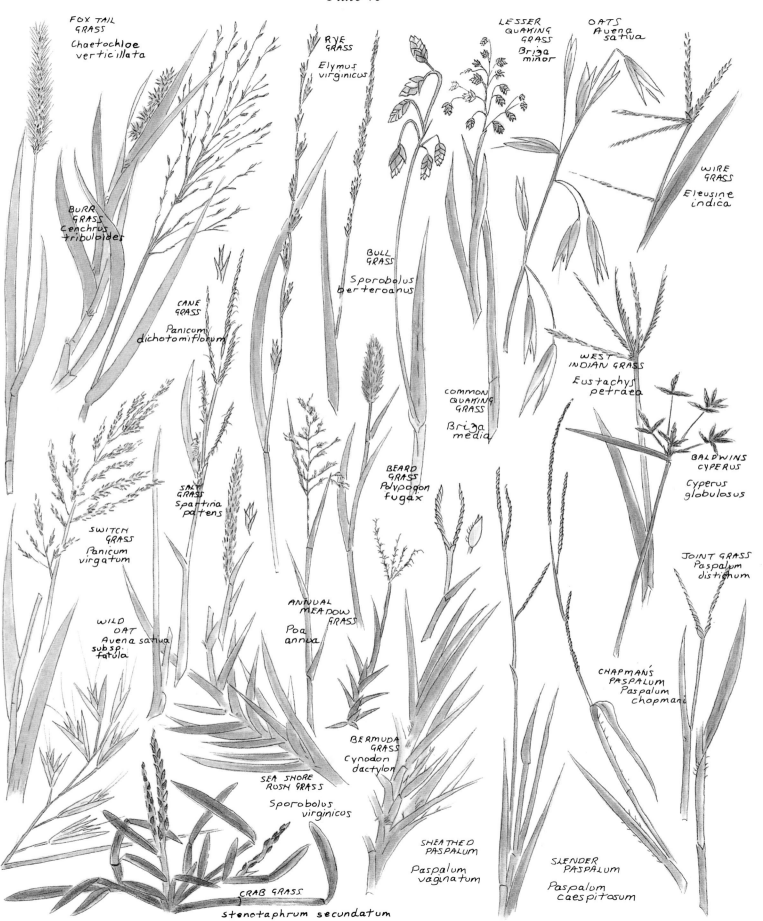

FOX TAIL GRASS
Chaetochloe verticillata

BURR GRASS
Cenchrus tribuloides

CANE GRASS
Panicum dichotomiflorum

SWITCH GRASS
Panicum virgatum

SALT GRASS
Spartina patens

WILD OAT
Avena sativa subsp. fatula

RYE GRASS
Elymus virginicus

BULL GRASS
Sporobolus berteroanus

BEARD GRASS
Polypogon fugax

ANNUAL MEADOW GRASS
Poa annua

COMMON QUAKING GRASS
Briza media

LESSER QUAKING GRASS
Briza minor

BERMUDA GRASS
Cynodon dactylon

SEA SHORE RUSH GRASS
Sporobolus virginicus

SHEATHED PASPALUM
Paspalum vaginatum

CRAB GRASS
Stenotaphrum secundatum

OATS
Avena sativa

WIRE GRASS
Eleusine indica

WEST INDIAN GRASS
Eustachys petraea

BALDWINS CYPERUS
Cyperus globulosus

JOINT GRASS
Paspalum distichum

CHAPMAN'S PASPALUM
Paspalum chapmani

SLENDER PASPALUM
Paspalum caespitosum

Pomegranate

Punica granatum　　　　　Punicaceae

Native in south-east Europe through to the Himalayas. A small tree with shining oblong leaves. The flowers are orange. Edible fruits are orange-biscuit colour with hard skin, the fruit membranes divide and contain fleshy seeds. The juice is used in the making of grenadine syrup. First mentioned in Bermuda in the 1600s, the fruits were dried and eaten like nuts, the rind was used to prepare leather as it contains tannin for dyeing. The bark was boiled and used for labour pains.

Christophine

Sechium edule　　　　　Cucurbitaceae

Locally seen scrambling over large trees in semi-wooded, overgrown gardens. The fruit is cooked as a vegetable, the tubers are also edible.

Mulberry

Morus nigra　　　　　Moraceae

A native of west Asia. Trees grow up to 25 feet tall. Flowers in drooping catkins followed by delicious red to black edible fruits. Bermuda has scattered specimens found in well-established gardens. Introduced into Bermuda in the early 1600s by settlers.

Peach

Prunus persica　　　　　Rosaceae

Originally from China where it is a major fruit crop. A small tree with delicate pink flowers and thin lanceolate leaves. White flesh and pink-pale yellow, furry skin. Introduced to Bermuda in the early 1800s and still grown in local gardens, occasionally wild in hedgerows. The peach leaf can produce a yellow dye, the juice may stain clothing.

Prickly Pear

Opuntia stricta var. *dillenii*　　　　　Cactaceae

Oblong, fleshy spine-covered pads distinguish the Prickly Pear from any other Bermudan plant. Large, golden-yellow flowers are followed by crimson-purple fruits with bunches of tiny stinging prickly hairs. Probably introduced to Bermuda by birds. Locals make jelly but not an easy fruit to crop. The juice can be used for a scarlet dye. Historically a candy was produced locally from fruit pulp.

Sugar Apple

Annona squamosa　　　　　Annonaceae

Occasionally called the sour sop but known in Bermuda as the 'Sugar Apple'. Originated in Central America and the West Indies. Leathery, oval leaves, cream-green flowers. The fruits are covered with large prominent knobs. These small divisions fall apart when the fruit is ripe. The custard yellow-white interior has a unique taste. First mentioned in Bermuda's records in 1829, it is not widely planted.

Grape

Vitis vinifera　　　　　Vitaceae

The wine grape came originally from the Caucasus and was known in Ancient Egypt and cultivated from 6000 years ago. A woody deciduous vine with climbing tendrils, 3-5 lobed leaves. Green flowers, sweet green fruits. Quite commonly found in temperate areas of Europe and California. The original grape was a wild grape.

Natal Plum

Carissa grandiflora　　　　　Apocynaceae

A woody shrub with conspicuous forked spines. Originating from Natal and India. Ovate leaves, pale through dark leathery leaves. Flowers waxy white, very fragrant, followed by scarlet fruits that are edible when ripe and contain black seeds. A popular hedging plant which is good at withstanding salt. Can reach a height of 18 feet.

Guava

Psidium guajava　　　　　Myrtaceae

An attractive evergreen tree which grows up to 30 feet. The trunk has a patchwork effect, white bark. A small tree with yellow edible fruits used in jams and jellies. In the early 1970s it became naturalized in Paget Marsh where it seriously threatened the endemic flora. Only very intensive culling operations managed to control and restrict its spread.

Banana (edible)

Musa acuminata x paradisiaca　　　　　Musaceae

The common Banana has spirally arranged leaves produced on a slender succulent trunk. Hanging bunches of cream-yellow flowers with red-violet bracts are followed by delicious yellow bananas 18 months from planting. As the plant begins to die new suckers produce the next generation of plants. Introduced to Bermuda around 1616, the Islands are now almost self-sufficient for much of the year. Locally a few craftpersons make traditional banana-leaved dolls. The leaves were once used for stuffing mattresses, and as a remedy for burns.

Avocado Pear

Persea americana　　　　　Lauraceae

From the West Indies, Guatemala and Mexico. Large tree with spreading leathery leaves, small greenish flowers, large, fleshy pear-shaped fruit with case, green-purple colours when ripe. Flesh green-yellow and eaten served in salads of many forms.

Lemon

Citrus limon 'Meyeri'　　　　　Rutaceae

The wild lemon from southern Asia found growing in established gardens, known locally as the rough lemon. The branches are thorny, the leaves ovate, flowers in pairs on the axils, petals white with purple markings, fruit very sour. A small round-headed tree, rarely exceeding 12-15 feet high. Sweet, fragrant white flowers have delicate scent. Seeds originally sent to Bermuda in 1616. Lemons are known to have more acid in their pulp than any other member of the citrus family. Other cultivated citrus crops on the Islands are Lemon, Lime, Orange and Grapefruits. From the sub-tropical Mediterranean countries, all have sweet, fragrant, waxy, white flowers and edible fruits.

Lime

Citrus aurantifolia　　　　　Rutaceae

Citrus are all of similar structure and form but come in various types of sour to sweet flavours and size, colour of skin varies. Normally small trees. Locally Lime is known as the Barbados Lime and has no real seed to mention. A small, thorny tree with an aromatic smell. White, waxy flowers and many uses in food and drinks.

Paw-Paw

Carica papaya　　　　　Caricaceae

Originally from Colombia. A small tree having stout but succulent trunk. Digital leaves with seven distinct lobes. Flowers greenish-yellow followed by fruits attached to the upper stem. These may be eaten when green as a vegetable or when ripe yellow as a fruit. A well-known meat tenderizer, it also has important medicinal properties, one being a value in reducing high blood pressure.

Orange

Citrus sinensis　　　　　Rutaceae

Originally from Brazil. The largest of Bermuda's Oranges is locally known as the Washington Navel. It's very sweet, juicy and has a long ripening period. The flowers, in large fragrant clusters, are white, waxy and seen from January to February. Citrus seeds were sent to Bermuda in 1616 and soon became a popular crop. The thick skin may still be green when the inside fruit is edible and delicious.

Locust and Wild Honey (Ceriman; Swiss Cheese Plant)

Monstera deliciosa　　　　　Araceae

Originally from south-central America, Mexico and Guatemala. A stout, woody-stemmed, close-jointed climbing plant with long, hanging, cord-like aerial roots. The large, glossy green leaves have segmented cuts and oblong holes creating distinct patterns. The white, upright flower spath encloses the delicious edible fruit, which has a pineapple-like aroma, a furry texture and should be eaten only when the scales open. The strong aerial roots cling to tree trunks or walls.

The kiss of the sun for pardon
The song of the birds for mirth
One is nearer God's heart
in a garden
Than anywhere else on Earth.

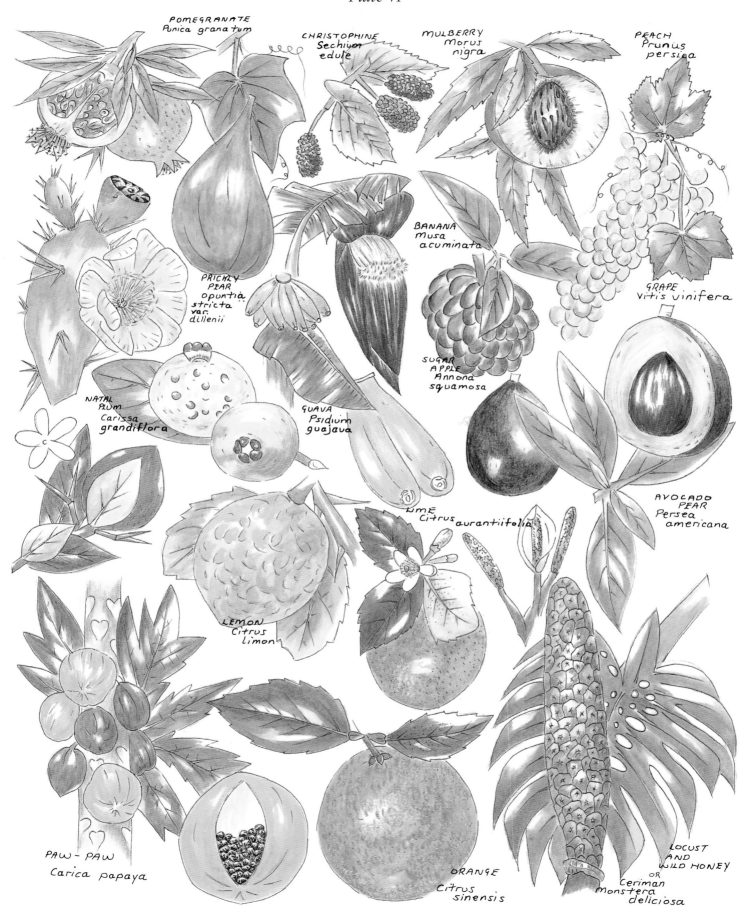

POMEGRANATE
Punica granatum

CHRISTOPHINE
Sechium
edule

MULBERRY
Morus
nigra

PEACH
Prunus
persica

PRICKLY
PEAR
Opuntia
stricta
var.
dillenii

BANANA
Musa
acuminata

GRAPE
Vitis vinifera

NATAL
PLUM
Carissa
grandiflora

SUGAR
APPLE
Annona
squamosa

GUAVA
Psidium
guajava

AVOCADO
PEAR
Persea
americana

LIME
Citrus aurantiifolia

LEMON
Citrus
limon

PAW-PAW
Carica papaya

ORANGE
Citrus
sinensis

LOCUST
AND
WILD HONEY
OR
Ceriman
Monstera
deliciosa

Bermuda has over 140 roses listed in the lovely Bermuda Rose Society's guide to the Old Bermuda Roses. Most gardens have at least one rose and many have incredible masses – collecting the Old Rose is a passion that can consume one's free time. Roses began to grace Bermuda's shores with the first settlers. I have included 12 of the historically interesting and personal favourites that grow locally. Roses can be found growing all over the world, from temperate climates to tropical mountains. Along with their obvious beauty they are sources of essential oils, medicine, etc. Worldwide there are thousands of roses, from ancient to modern with so many crosses between them no one quite knows how many there are exactly. Bermuda is fortunate in having a unique collection of old established roses and much tender care is required to keep them from other invading plants.

China Roses
Rosa chinensis sp.

Old Blush Parsons Pink
Rosa chinensis sp. Rosaceae
One of the old stud roses growing up to 4 feet. Small sprays of flowers in two tones of pink. Small flowers 2¹/₂ inches across.

Agrippina Cramoisi Superieur (1832)
Rosa chinensis sp. Rosaceae
China Rose known as the Old Bermuda Red Rose found in many gardens islandwide, growing in a bush or climbing form. Crimson-red flowers seem to bloom all year. Six feet high.

Green Rose
Rosa chinenis viridiflora Rosaceae
Upright bush up to 5 feet. Small, double green flowers with streaked bronze markings 1¹/₂ inches across. Another year long bloomer.

Shell Rose Duchesse de Brabant (1857) – Tea Rose
Rosa odorata sp. Rosaceae
Known locally as the 'Shell Rose' reaching a height of 5 feet. Double flowers, mostly soft pink, up to 3 inches across but can be deeper pink depending on growing conditions.

Macartney Rose
Rosa bracteata (1793) Rosaceae
Known locally as the Fried Egg. Pure white flowers with bright yellow stamens 4 inches or more across. Very prickly. Loves to scramble and root itself along old walls.

Kathleen 'Mystery Rose'
Rosa hybrid musk (1922) Rosaceae
Seems to enjoy growing in a bush form or along trellis, up to 5 feet. Pink blooms and lovely rose hips for flower arranging.

Belfield Rose
Rosa chinenisis semperflorens Rosaceae
Also known as Slaters Crimson China 1792. After much interest and propagation many rose growers now own this rose. Slow growing bush up to 3 feet, single, deep crimson-red flowers 2 inches across.

Archduke Charles (Seven Sisters) (1840)
Rosa chinensis sp. Rosaceae
Known locally as the Seven Sisters. Found in many old Bermudan gardens, up to 6 feet. Blooms most of the year, flowers opening pink-crimson going darker with age, 3 inches across.

Smiths Parish 'Mystery Rose'
Rosa chinensis sp. Rosaceae
Growing into a full bush 6 feet high, small cupped flowers 1¹/₂ inches across with a deep pink streak within the petals. Another lasting bloomer!

Spice Humes Blush (Tea Scented China)
Tea Rose (1760)
Rosa odorata sp. Rosaceae
Very popular locally, because of its strong scent called the Spicy Rose. Reaching a height of 4 feet, deep pink buds opening to light pink flower that fades to white, 2-3 inches across.

Mutabilis
Rosa chinensis mutabilis (1896) Rosaceae
Widely grown, scrambles a little. A large bush up to 5 feet high. The buds are shades of orange, yellow-pink. Flowers 3¹/₂ inches across, seems to flower most of the year.

Lamarque
Rosa noisette (1830) Rosaceae
Pure white flowers, 3 inches across, lovely fragrance, quite short stems.

The Rose is a rose
And was always a rose
But the theory now goes
That the apple's a rose
And the pear is, and so's the
plum I suppose.
The dear only knows
what will next prove a rose.
You, of course, are a rose
But were always a rose.

Robert Frost 1874-1963

Roses

Plate 42

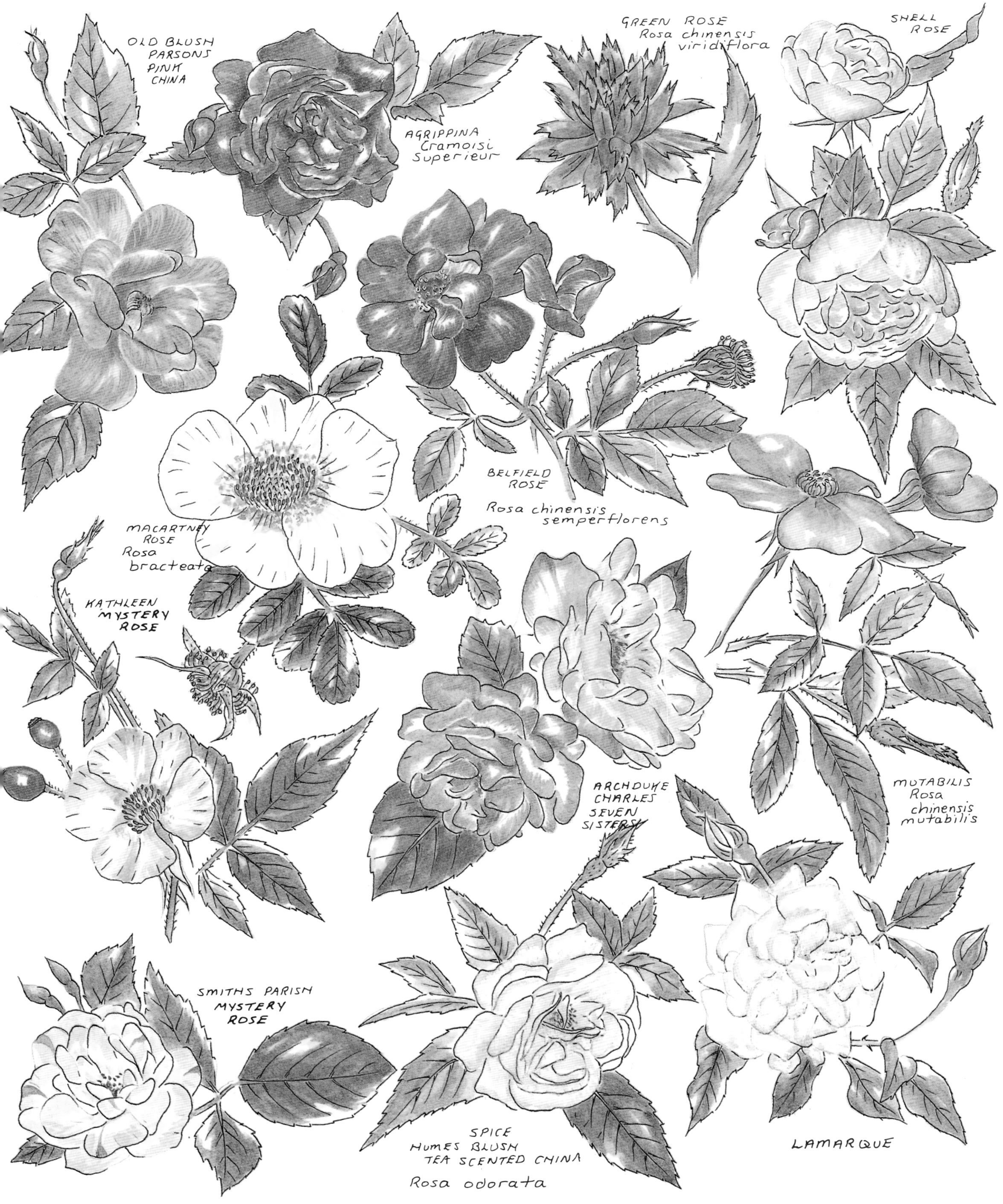
OLD BLUSH
PARSONS
PINK
CHINA
AGRIPPINA
Cramoisi
Superieur
GREEN ROSE
Rosa chinensis
viridiflora
SHELL
ROSE
BELFIELD
ROSE
Rosa chinensis
semperflorens
MACARTNEY
ROSE
Rosa
bracteata
KATHLEEN
MYSTERY
ROSE
ARCHDUKE
CHARLES
SEVEN
SISTERS
MUTABILIS
Rosa
chinensis
mutabilis
SMITHS PARISH
MYSTERY
ROSE
SPICE
HUMES BLUSH
TEA SCENTED CHINA
Rosa odorata
LAMARQUE

Index

Catharanthus roseus	Madagascar Periwinkle	Apocynaceae	20
Celtis laevigata	Southern Hackberry	Ulmaceae	3
Cenchrus tribuloides	Burr Grass	Gramineae	40
Centaurium pulchellum	Pink Centurium	Gentianaceae	11
Cerastium cerastoides	Mouse-Ear Chickweed	Caryophyllaceae	11
Cerastium vulgatum	Large Mouse-Ear Chickweed	Caryophyllaceae	11
Ceratophyllum demersum	Ditchweed (Hornwort)	Ceratophyllaceae	8
Cestrum nocturnum	Cestrum (Lady of the Night)	Solanaceae	13
Chaetochloe verticillata	Fox Tail Grass	Gramineae	40
Chamaerops humilis	European Fan Palm	Palmae	28
Chamaesyce hirta	Hairy Spurge	Euphorbiaceae	12
Chamaesyce hypericifolia	Hypericum Leaved Spurge	Euphorbiaceae	12
Chamaesyce prostrata	Prostrate Spurge	Euphorbiaceae	10
Chenopodium album	Pig Weed	Chenopodiaceae	12
Chicorium intybus	Chicory	Compositae	15
Chiococca bermudiana	Bermuda Snowberry	Rubiaceae	4
Chrysalidocarpus lutescens	Butterfly/Bamboo Palm	Palmae	26
Chrysanthemum leucanthemum	White Daisy	Compositae	11
Cissus sicyoides	West Indian Cissus	Vitaceae	16
Citharexylum spinosum	Fiddlewood	Verbenaceae	30
Citrus aurantiifolia	Lime	Rutaceae	41
Citrus limon 'Meyeri'	Lemon	Rutaceae	41
Citrus sinensis	Orange	Rutaceae	41
Clematis flammula	Traveller's Joy	Ranunculaceae	17
Clinopodium calamintha	Calamint	Labiatae	15
Clitoria ternata	Blue Pea	Leguminosae	19
Coccoloba uvifera	Bay Grape	Polygonaceae	2
Cocos nucifera	Coconut Palm	Palmae	26
Codiaeum variegatum	Croton	Euphorbiaceae	22
Commelina longicaulis	Creeping Day Flower	Commelinaceae	10
Conocarpus erectus	Buttonwood	Combretaceae	2
Cordia dentata	White Cordia	Boraginaceae	33
Cordia sebestena	Scarlet Cordia	Boraginaceae	33
Crescentia cujeta	Calabash Tree	Bignoniaceae	36
Crinum angustum	Crinum Lily	Amaryllidaceae	21
Crossopetalum rhacoma (syn. *Myginda crossopetalum*, syn. *Rhacoma crossopetalum*)	Rhacoma	Celastraceae	5
Crotalaria spectabilis	Rattle Box	Leguminosae	1
Croton punctatus	Beach Croton	Euphorbiaceae	6
Ctenitis sloanei	Bermuda Cave Fern	Aspleniaceae	39
Cupressus sempervirens	Italian Cypress	Cuppressaceae	30
Cycas circinalis	Sago Palm	Cycadaceae	24
Cycas revoluta	Sago Palm (Japanese)	Cycadaceae	24
Cymbalaria muralis	Coliseum Ivy	Scrophulariaceae	10
Cynodon dactylon	Bermuda Grass	Gramineae	40
Cyperus alternifolius	Umbrella Plant	Cyperaceae	23
Cyperus esculentus	Yellow Nut Grass	Cyperaceae	23
Cyperus globulosus	Baldwins Cyperus	Cyperaceae	40
Cyrtomium falcatum	Holly Fern	Dryopteridaceae	39
Datura aurea (syn. *Brugmansia aurea*)	Angels' Trumpets	Solanaceae	31
Delonix regia	Royal Poinciana	Leguminosae	38
Desmodium canadense	Showy Tick Trefoil	Leguminosae	8
Dictyosperma album	Princess Palm	Palmae	27
Diplazium laffanianum	Governor Laffan's Fern	Woodsiaceae	39
Dodonaea viscosa	Jamaica Dogwood	Sapindaceae	4
Dombeya wallichii	Dombeya	Sterculiaceae	31
Dracaena arborea	Tree Dracaena	Liliaceae	23
Dracaena marginata	Madagascar Dragon Tree	Liliaceae	23
Dryopteris bermudiana	Bermuda Shield Fern	Aspleniaceae	39
Dryopteris normalis	Large Marsh Shield Fern	Polypodiaceae	39
Duranta erecta (syn. *Duranta repens*)	Pigeon Berry	Verbenaceae	19
Elaeagnus angustifolia	Elaeagnus	Elaeagnaceae	29
Eleocharis bermudiana	Bermuda Spike Rush	Cyperaceae	1
Eleocharis interstincta	Knotted Spike Rush	Cyperaceae	7
Eleocharis rostellata	Beaked Spike Rush	Cyperaceae	8
Eleusine indica	Wire Grass	Gramineae	40
Elymus virginicus	Rye Grass	Gramineae	40
Epilobium obscurum	Thin Runner Willow Herb	Onagraceae	9
Erigeron annus	Daisy Fleabane	Compositae	11
Erigeron darrellianus	Darrells Fleabane	Compositae	1
Eriobotrya japonica	Loquat (Japanese)	Rosaceae	33
Erysimum officinale	Hedge Mustard	Cruciferae	11
Erythrina caffra	Sword Tree (Coral Tree)	Leguminosae	37
Eucalyptus camaldulensis	Red River Gum Tree	Myrtaceae	34
Eugenia monticola (syn. *Eugenia axillaris*)	White Stopper	Myrtaceae	4
Eugenia uniflora	Surinam Cherry	Myrtaceae	36
Eupatorium adenophorum	Glandular Eupatorium	Compositae	7
Eupatorium riparium	Small White Eupatorium	Compositae	7
Euphorbia buxifolia	Coast Spurge	Euphorbiaceae	6
Euphorbia heterophylla	Joseph's Coat (Japanese Poinsettia)	Euphorbiaceae	10
Euphorbia milii var. splendens	Crown of Thorns	Euphorbiaceae	22
Euphorbia pulcherrima	Poinsettia	Euphorbiaceae	22
Euphorbia tirucalli	Milk Bush (Pencil Tree)	Euphorbiaceae	29
Eustachys petraea (syn. *Chloris petraea*)	West Indian Grass	Gramineae	40
Ficus benghalensis	Ban Yan Tree	Moraceae	32
Ficus benjamina	Weeping Fig	Moraceae	32
Ficus carica	Edible Fig	Moraceae	31
Ficus elastica	Indian Rubber Tree	Moraceae	32

Valerianodes jamaicensis	Jamaica Vervain	Verbenaceae	10
Verbascum virgatum	Twiggy Mullein	Scrophulariaceae	15
Verbena alba	Marsh Eclipta	Verbenaceae	7
Verbena bonariensis	South American Vervain	Verbenaceae	9
Verbena rigida	Stiff Verbena	Verbenaceae	11
Veronica arvensis	Wall Speedwell	Scrophulariaceae	10
Vicia angustifolia	Narrow-Leaved Vetch	Leguminosae	11
Vicia cracca	Tufted Vetch	Leguminosae	9
Vicia sylvatica	Wood Vetch	Leguminosae	9
Viola odorata	Sweet Violet	Violaceae	12
Vitis vinifera	Common Grape Vine	Vitaceae	41
Washingtonia filifera	Washingtonia Palm	Palmae	27
Wedelia trilobata	Wedelia	Compositae	18
Woodwardia virginica	Virginia Chain Fern	Polypodiaceae	39
Yucca aloifolia	Spanish Bayonet	Agavaceae	5 & 6
Zantedeschia aethiopica	Calla Lily (White)	Araceae	21
Zanthoxylum flavum	Yellowwood	Rutaceae	3
Zephyranthes atamasco 'Album'	White Atamasco Lily	Liliaceae	20
Zephyranthes atamasco	Purple Atamasco Lily	Liliaceae	20
Zephyranthes atamasco	Yellow Atamasco Lily	Liliaceae	20
Zeuxine strateumatica	Terrestrial Orchid	Orchidaceae	8

English names

African Blue Lily	Agapanthus africanus	Liliaceae	21
African Tulip Tree	Spathodea campanulata	Bignoniaceae	35
Agave	Agave americana marginata	Agavaceae	23
Agave Sisal Hemp	Agave sisalana	Agavaceae	23
Alexanders	Smyrnium olusatrum	Umbelliferae	15
Allamanda	Allamanda cathartica	Apocynaceae	19
Allspice	Pimenta dioica	Myrtaceae	30
Aloe sp.	Aloe	Aloeaceae	23
Aloe Bitter	Aloe succotrina	Liliaceae	23
Angels' Trumpets	Datura aurea (syn. Brugmansia aurea)	Solanaceae	31
Annual Meadow Grass	Poa annua	Gramineae	40
Apple of Peru (Shoo Fly Plant)	Nicandra physaloides	Solanaceae	9
Arrow Leaved Morning Glory	Ipomoea sagittata	Convolvulaceae	16
Arrowroot	Maranta arundinaceae	Marantaceae	21
Asparagus Fern	Asparagus densiflorus	Liliaceae	39
Australian Ban Yan	Ficus macrophylla	Moraceae	32
Avocado Pear	Persea americana	Lauraceae	41
Baldwins Chickweed	Stellaria baldwinii	Caryophyllaceae	11
Baldwins Cyperus	Cyperus globulosus	Cyperaceae	40
Balloon Vine	Cardiospermum halicacabum	Sapindaceae	10
Bamboo Cane	Gigantochola vertiallata	Gramineae	23
Bamboo Palm (Butterfly Palm)	Chrysalidocarpus lutescens	Palmae	26
Banana (edible)	Musa acuminata x.paradisiaca	Musaceae	41
Ban Yan Tree	Ficus benghalensis	Moraceae	32
Barbados Gooseberry	Pereskia aculeata	Cactaceae	19
Bauhinia	Bauhinia acuminata	Leguminosae	37
Bay Bean	Canavali lineata	Leguminosae	6
Bay Grape	Coccoloba uvifera	Polygonaceae	2
Beach Alternanthera	Achyranthes maritima	Amaranthaceae	8
Beach Croton	Croton punctatus	Euphorbiaceae	6
Beach Lobelia	Scaevola plumieri	Goodeniaceae	6
Beaked Spike Rush	Elocharis rostellata	Cyperaceae	8
Beard Grass	Andropogon glomeratus	Gramineae	7
Beard Grass	Polypogon fugax	Gramineae	40
Bear's Foot	Polymnia uvedalia	Compositae	9
Bermuda Bean	Phaseolus lignosus	Leguminosae	1
Bermuda Bedstraw	Galium bermudense	Rubiaceae	1
Bermuda Buttercup	Oxalis pes-caprae	Oxalidaceae	14
Bermuda Campylopus (moss)	Campylopus bermudianus	Dicranaceae	1
Bermuda Cave Fern	Ctenitis sloanei	Aspleniaceae	39
Bermuda Cedar (Bermuda Juniper)	Juniperus bermudiana	Cupressaceae	2
Bermuda Easter Lily	Lilium longiflorum var. ensiforme	Liliaceae	21
Bermuda Grass	Cynodon dactylon	Gramineae	40
Bermuda Olivewood	Cassine laneana (syn. Elaeodendron laneanum)	Celastraceae	3
Bermuda Palmetto	Sabal bermudana	Palmae	28
Bermuda Sedge	Carex bermudiana	Cyperaceae	8
Bermuda Shield Fern	Dryopteris bermudiana	Aspleniaceae	39
Bermuda Snowberry	Chiococca bermudiana	Rubiaceae	4
Bermuda Spike Rush	Eleocharis bermudiana	Cyperaceae	1
Bermuda Trichostomum (moss)	Trichostomum bermudanum	Pottaiceae	1
Bermudiana	Sisyrinchium bermudiana	Iridaceae	1
Bird of Paradise	Strelitzia reginae	Strelitziaceae	21
Bird Pepper	Capsicum baccatum	Solanaceae	12
Black Ebony	Albizia lebbeck	Leguminosae	38
Black Mangrove	Avicennia nitida	Verbenaceae	2
Black Medic	Medicago lupulina	Leguminosae	11
Black Nightshade	Solanum nigrum	Solanaceae	12
Blue Pea	Clitoria ternata	Leguminosae	19
Blue Pimpernel	Anagallis arvensis var. caerulea	Primulaceae	11

English Plantain	*Plantago lanceolata*	Plantaginaceae	15
English Sage Red (Wild Sage Bush)	*Lantana camara*	Verbenaceae	15
European Fan Palm	*Chamaerops humilis*	Palmae	28
Everlasting Senna	*Senna floribunda*	Leguminosae	31
	(syn. *Cassia floribunda*)		
False Garlic	*Nothoscordum gracile*	Liliaceae	20
False Mallow	*Malvastrum coromandelianum*	Malvaceae	9
False Nettle	*Boehmeria cylindrica*	Urticaceae	9
Fennel	*Foeniculum vulgare*	Umbelliferae	15
Fern Asparagus	*Asparagus setaceus*	Liliaceae	39
Fiddle Leaf Fig	*Ficus lyrata*	Moraceae	32
Fiddlewood	*Citharexylum spinosum*	Verbenaceae	30
Field Woundwort	*Stachys arvensis*	Labiatae	9
Fiji Fan Palm	*Pritchardia pacifica*	Palmae	28
Fine-leaved Sandwort	*Minuartia hybrida*	Caryophyllaceae	11
Fishtail Palm	*Caryota urens*	Palmae	25
Flame Tree	*Brachychiton acerifolius*	Sterculiaceae	37
Flopper (Life Plant)	*Bryophyllum pinnatum*	Crassulaceae	14
Forestiera	*Forestiera segregata*	Oleaceae	3
Fox Tail Grass	*Chaetochloe verticillata*	Gramineae	40
Frangipani Pink	*Plumeria rubra*	Apocynaceae	33
Frangipani White	*Plumeria alba*	Apocynaceae	33
Freesia	*Freesia refracta-alba*	Iridaceae	14
Fumitory	*Fumaria muralis*	Fumariaceae	11
Gaillardia (Fire Wheels)	*Gaillardia pulchella*	Compositae	20
Gallant Soldier	*Galinsoga parviflora*	Compositae	9
Garden Black Nightshade	*Solanum nigrum*	Solanaceae	12
Garden Parsley	*Petroselinum crispum*	Umbelliferae	15
Gazania	*Gazania ringens var. uniflora*	Compositae	20
Geranium (Zonal Pelargonium)	*Pelargonium x. hortorum*	Geraniaceae	20
Giant Bamboo Cane 'Bambusa'	*Gigantochola vertiallata*	Gramineae	23
Giant False Agave	*Furcraea gigantea*	Amaryllidaceae	23
Giant Flowered Magnolia	*Magnolia grandiflora*	Magnoliaceae	34
Giant Leather Fern	*Acrostichum danaeifolium*	Pteridaceae	39
	(syn. *Acrostichum excelsum*)		
Giant Privet	*Ligustrum lucidum*	Oleaceae	29
Glandular Eupatorium	*Eupatorium adenophorum*	Compositae	7
Golden Shower	*Cassia fistula*	Leguminosae	35
Governor Laffan's Fern	*Diplazium laffanianum*	Woodsiaceae	39
Grape	*Vitis vinifera*	Vitaceae	41
Great American Bullrush	*Schoenoplectus vallidus*	Cyperaceae	23
Great Plantain (Common)	*Plantago major*	Plantaginaceae	15
Guava	*Psidium guajava*	Myrtaceae	41
Hairy Horse-Weed	*Leptilon linifolium*	Carduaceae	12
Hairy Spurge	*Chamaesyce hirta*	Euphorbiaceae	12
Heath Fire Cracker	*Russelia equisetiformis*	Scrophulariaceae	7
Hedge Mustard	*Erysimum officinale*	Cruciferae	11
Henbit (Dead Nettle)	*Lamium amplexicaule*	Labiatae	9
Hibiscus	*Hibiscus rosa sinensis*	Malvaceae	19
Holly Fern	*Cyrtomium falcatum*	Dryopteridaceae	39
Horse-Weed Fleabane	*Leptilon canadense*	Carduaceae	12
Hypericum-Leaved Spurge	*Chamaesyce hypericifolia*	Euphorbiaceae	12
Ice Plant	*Carpobrotus edulis*	Aizoaceae	18
Indian Laurel	*Ficus retusa*	Moraceae	32
Indian Mallow	*Abutilon theophrasti*	Malvaceae	7
Indian Rubber Tree	*Ficus elastica*	Moraceae	32
Ink Berry (Small Passion Flower)	*Passiflora suberosa*	Passifloraceae	19
Iodine Bush (Sea Lavender)	*Mallotonia gnaphalodes*	Baraginaceae	6
Italian Cypress	*Cupressus sempervirens*	Cupressaceae	30
Jacaranda	*Jacaranda mimosifolia*	Bignoniaceae	38
Jamaica Dogwood	*Dodonaea viscosa*	Sapindaceae	4
Jamaica Vervain	*Valerianodes jamaicensis*	Verbenaceae	10
Jamaica Weed	*Nama jamaicense*	Hydrophyllaceae	9
Japanese Pittosporum	*Pittosporum undulatum*	Pittosporaceae	29
Jasmine	*Jasminum simplicifolium*	Oleaceae	19
Jerusalem Thorn	*Parkinsonia aculeata*	Leguminosae	33
Joint Grass	*Paspalum distichum*	Gramineae	40
Joseph's Coat (Japanese Poinsettia)	*Euphorbia heterophylla*	Euphorbiaceae	10
Jumbie Bean (Wild Mimosa)	*Leucaena leucocephala*	Leguminosae	13
Kalanchoe	*Kalanchoe flammea*	Crassulaceae	20
King's Mantle	*Thunbergia erecta*	Acanthaceae	18
Knotted Hedge Parsley	*Torilis nodosa*	Umbelliferae	15
Knotted Spike Rush	*Eleocharis interstincta*	Cyperaceae	7
Kumani	*Calophyllum inophyllum*	Guttiferaceae	34
Lace Plant (Artillery Plant)	*Pilea microphylla*	Urticaceae	20
Ladies Tresses Orchid	*Spiranthes spiralis*	Orchidaceae	8
Lady of the Night	*Brunfelsia americana*	Solanaceae	22
Lady Palm	*Rhapis excelsa*	Palmae	25
Lamarcks Trema	*Trema lamarckiana*	Ulmaceae	4
Large Marsh Shield Fern	*Dryopteris normalis*	Polypodiaceae	39
Large Mouse Ear Chickweed	*Cerastium vulgatum*	Caryophyllaceae	11
Lemon	*Citrus limon 'Meyeri'*	Rutaceae	41
Lesser Bullrush (Cattail)	*Typha angustifolia*	Gramineae	8
Lesser Quaking Grass	*Briza minor*	Gramineae	40

Thin Runner Willowherb	*Epilobium obscurum*	Onagraceae	9
Thunbergia (Purple Allamanda)	*Thunbergia grandiflora*	Acanthaceae	18
Tobacco	*Nicotiana tabacum*	Solanaceae	12
Toothed Medic	*Medicago polymorpha*	Leguminosae	11
Toothed Spleenwort	*Asplenium dentatum*	Aspleniaceae	39
Traveller's Joy	*Clematis flammula*	Ranunculaceae	17
Traveller's Tree	*Ravenala madagascariensis*	Strelitziaceae	24
Tree Dracaena	*Dracaena arborea*	Liliaceae	23
Tree Hibiscus	*Thespesia populnea*	Malvaceae	37
True Aloe	*Aloe vera*	Aloeaceae	23
Trumpet Honeysuckle	*Lonicera sempervirens*	Caprifoliaceae	19
Tufted Vetch	*Vicia cracca*	Leguminosae	9
Turkey Berry	*Callicarpa americana*	Verbenaceae	1
Turnera (West Indian Holly)	*Turnera ulmifolia*	Turneraceae	1
Twiggy Mullein	*Verbascum virgatum*	Scrophulariaceae	15
Umbrella Plant	*Cyperus alternifolius*	Cyperaceae	23
Variegated Pittosporum	*Pittosporum tobira variegata*	Pittosporaceae	29
Varnish Tree	*Koelreuteria paniculata*	Sapindaceae	33
Veined (Stiff) Verbena	*Verbena rigida*	Verbenaceae	11
Victoria Box	*Pittosporum tobira*	Pittosporaceae	29
Virgate Mimosa	*Leucaena virgatum*	Leguminosae	13
Virginia Chain Fern	*Woodwardia virginica*	Polypodiaceae	39
Virginia Creeper	*Parthenocissus quinquefolia*	Vitaceae	17
Wall Speedwell	*Veronica arvensis*	Scrophulariaceae	10
Wandering Jew	*Tradescantia fluminensis*	Commelinaceae	18
Washingtonia Palm	*Washingtonia filifera*	Palmae	27
Water Fern	*Salvinia rotundifolia*	Salviniaceae	8
Wax Myrtle	*Myrica cerifera*	Myrtaceae	5
Wedelia	*Wedelia trilobata*	Compositae	18
Weeping Fig	*Ficus benjamina*	Moraceae	32
West Indian Almond	*Terminalia catappa*	Combretaceae	35
West Indian Cissus	*Cissus sicyoides*	Vitaceae	16
West Indian Grass	*Eustachys petraea* (syn. *Chloris petraea*)	Gramineae	40
White Atamasco Lily	*Zephyranthes atamasco* 'Album'	Liliaceae	20
White Beggars' Ticks	*Bidens pilosa*	Compositae	10
White Cedar (Trumpet Tree)	*Tabebuia pallida*	Bignoniaceae	34
White Cordia	*Cordia dentata*	Boraginaceae	33
White Daisy	*Chrysanthemum leucanthemum*	Compositae	11
White Morning Glory	*Ipomoea alba*	Convolvulaceae	16
White Morning Glory	*Turbinia corymbosa*	Convolvulaceae	16
White Stopper	*Eugenia monticola* (syn. *Eugenia axillaris*)	Myrtaceae	4
Widgeon Grass (Beaked Tasselweed)	*Ruppia maritima*	Ruppiaceae	8
Wild Bermuda Pepper	*Peperomia septentrionalis*	Piperaceae	1
Wild Coffee Shrub	*Psychotria undata*	Rubiaceae	4
Wild Indigo	*Indigofera suffruticosa*	Leguminosae	15
Wild Mimosa (Jumbie Bean)	*Leucaena leucocephala*	Leguminosae	13
Wild Oat	*Avena sativa* (sub sp. *fatula*)	Gramineae	40
Wild Pepper Grass	*Lepidium campestre*	Cruciferae	11
Wild Stock	*Matthiola incana*	Cruciferae	6
Wild Sage Bush (Shrub Verbena)	*Lantana camara*	Verbenaceae	15
Wire Grass	*Eleusine indica*	Gramineae	40
Wire Weed	*Sida carpinifolia*	Malvaceae	10
Wood Cudweed	*Gnaphalium sylvaticum*	Compositae	9
Wood Grass	*Oplismenus hirtellus*	Gramineae	8
Wood Sorrel	*Oxalis corniculata*	Oxalidaceae	14
Wood Vetch	*Vicia sylvatica*	Leguminosae	9
Woody Glasswort (Marsh Samphire)	*Salicornia europaea*	Chenopodiaceae	8
Yellow Atamasco Lily	*Zephyranthes atamasco*	Liliaceae	20
Yellow Japanese Honeysuckle	*Lonicera japonica*	Caprifoliaceae	18
Yellow Melilot	*Melilotus indica*	Leguminosae	11
Yellow Nut Grass	*Cyperus esculentus*	Cyperaceae	23
Yellow Oleander (Lucky Nut)	*Thevetia peruviana*	Apocynaceae	31
Yellow Poinciana	*Peltophorum pterocarpum*	Leguminosae	38
Yellow Tecoma	*Tecoma stans*	Bignoniaceae	31
Yellow Wood	*Zanthoxylum flavum*	Rutaceae	3
Yellow Wood Sorrel (Bermuda Buttercup)	*Oxalis pes-caprae*	Oxalidaceae	14
Yew 'Maki' (Big Leaf Podocarp)	*Podocarpus macrophyllus*	Podocarpaceae	29